THE PELICAN SHAKESPEARE
GENERAL EDITOR : ALFRED HARBAGE
ABI
MACBETH

WILLIAM SHAKESPEARE

The Tragedy of Macbeth

EDITED BY ALFRED HARBAGE

PENGUIN BOOKS

BALTIMORE · MARYLAND

This edition first published 1956
Reprinted 1960, 1962, 1964, 1966 (twice)
Penguin Books Inc.
7110 Ambassador Road, Baltimore, Maryland 21207

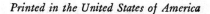

Printed in the United States of America

CONTENTS

CONTENTS

SHAKESPEARE AND HIS STAGE

William Shakespeare was christened in Holy Trinity Church, Stratford-on-Avon, April 26, 1564. His birth is traditionally assigned to April 23rd. He was the eldest of four boys and two girls who survived infancy in the family of John Shakespeare, glover and trader of Henley Street, and his wife Mary Arden, daughter of a small landowner of Wilmcote. In 1568 John was elected Bailiff (equivalent to Mayor) of Stratford, having already filled the minor municipal offices. The town maintained for the sons of the burgesses a free school, taught by a university graduate and offering preparation in Latin sufficient for university entrance; its early registers are lost, but there can be little doubt that Shakespeare received the formal part of his education in this school.

On November 27, 1582, a license was issued for the marriage of William Shakespeare (aged eighteen) and Ann Hathaway (aged twenty-six), and on May 26, 1583, their child Susanna was christened in Holy Trinity Church. The inference that the marriage was forced upon the youth is natural but not inevitable; betrothal was legally binding at the time, and was sometimes regarded as conferring conjugal rights. Two additional children of the marriage, the twins Hamnet and Judith, christened on February 2, 1585. Meanwhile the prosperity of the elder Shakespeares had declined, and William was impelled to seek a career outside Stratford.

The tradition that he spent some time as a country teacher is old but unverifiable. Because of the absence of records his early twenties are called the "lost years," and only one thing about them is certain – that at least some of these years were spent in winning a place in the acting profession. He may have begun as a provincial trouper, but by 1592 he was established in London and prominent enough to be attacked. In a pamphlet of that year, *Groatsworth of Wit,* the ailing Robert Greene complained of the neglect which university writers like himself had suffered from actors, one of whom was daring to set up as a playwright:

> . . . an upstart crow beautified with our feathers, that with his *Tiger's heart wrapt in a player's hide* supposes he is as well able to bombast out a blank verse as the best of you, and being an absolute Johannes-factotum, is in his own conceit the only Shake-scene in a country.

The pun on his name, and the parody of his line "O tiger's heart wrapt in a woman's hide" (*III Henry VI*), pointed clearly to Shakespeare. Some of his admirers protested, and Henry Chettle, the editor of Greene's pamphlet, saw fit to apologize:

> I am as sorry as if the original fault had been my fault, because myself have seen his demeanor no less civil than he excellent in the quality he professes. Besides divers of worship have reported his uprightness of dealing, which argues his honesty, and his facetious grace in writing that approves his art. (Prefatory epistle, *Kind Heart's Dream*)

The plague closed the London theatres for many months in 1593–94, denying the actors their livelihood. To this period belong Shakespeare's two narrative poems, *Venus and Adonis* and *Rape of Lucrece,* both dedicated to the Earl

8

of Southampton. No doubt the poet was rewarded with a gift of money as usual in such cases, but he did no further dedicating and we have no reliable information on whether Southampton, or anyone else, became his regular patron. His sonnets, first mentioned in 1598 and published without his consent in 1609, are intimate without being explicitly autobiographical. They seem to commemorate the poet's friendship with an idealized youth, rivalry with a more favored poet, and love affair with a dark mistress; and his bitterness when the mistress betrays him in conjunction with the friend; but it is difficult to decide precisely what the "story" is, impossible to decide whether it is fictional or true. The real distinction of the sonnets, at least of those not purely conventional, rests in the universality of the thoughts and moods they express, and in their poignancy and beauty.

In 1594 was formed the theatrical company known until 1603 as the Lord Chamberlain's Men, thereafter as the King's Men. Its original membership included, besides Shakespeare, the beloved clown Will Kempe and the famous actor Richard Burbage. The company acted in various London theatres and even toured the provinces, but it is chiefly associated in our minds with the Globe Theatre built on the south bank of the Thames in 1599. Shakespeare was an actor and joint owner of this company (and its Globe) through the remainder of his creative years. His plays, written at the average rate of two a year, together with Burbage's acting won it its place of leadership among the London companies.

Individual plays began to appear in print, in editions both honest and piratical, and the publishers became increasingly aware of the value of Shakespeare's name on the title pages. As early as 1598 he was hailed as the leading English dramatist in the *Palladis Tamia* of Francis Meres:

9

As Plautus and Seneca are accounted the best for Comedy and Tragedy among the Latins, so Shakespeare among the English is the most excellent in both kinds for the stage: for Comedy, witness his *Gentlemen of Verona*, his *Errors*, his *Love labors lost*, his *Love labors won [Taming of the Shrew?]*, his *Midsummers night dream*, & his *Merchant of Venice;* for Tragedy, his *Richard the 2*, *Richard the 3*, *Henry the 4*, *King John*, *Titus Andronicus*, and his *Romeo and Juliet*.

The note is valuable, both in indicating Shakespeare's prestige and in helping us to establish a chronology. In the second half of his writing career, history plays gave place to the great tragedies; and farces and light comedies gave place to the problem plays and symbolic romances. In 1623, seven years after his death, his former fellow actors, John Hemming and Henry Condell, cooperated with a group of London printers in bringing out his plays in collected form. The volume is generally known as the First Folio.

Shakespeare had never severed his relations with Stratford. His wife and children may sometimes have shared his London lodgings, but their home was Stratford. His son Hamnet was buried there in 1596, and his daughters Susanna and Judith were married there in 1607 and 1616 respectively. (His father, for whom he had secured a coat of arms and thus the privilege of writing himself gentleman, died in 1601, his mother in 1608.) His considerable earnings in London, as actor-sharer, part owner of the Globe, and playwright, were invested chiefly in Stratford property. In 1597 he purchased for £60 New Place, one of the two most imposing residences in the town. A number of other business transactions, as well as minor episodes in his career, have left documentary records. By 1611 he was in a position to retire, and he seems gradually to have withdrawn from theatrical activity in order to live in Stratford. In March, 1616, he made a will, leaving token bequests to Burbage, Hemming, and Condell, but the bulk of his estate to his family. The most famous feature of the will, the bequest of the second-best bed to his wife, reveals nothing about Shakespeare's marriage; the quaintness of the provision seems commonplace to those familiar with ancient testaments. Shakespeare died April 23, 1616, and was buried in the Stratford church where he had been christened. Within seven years a monument was erected to his memory on the north wall of the chancel. Its portrait bust and the Droeshout engraving on the title page of the First Folio provide the only likenesses with an established claim to authenticity. The best verbal vignette was written by his rival Ben Jonson, the more impressive for being imbedded in a context mainly critical:

> ... I loved the man, and do honor his memory (on this side idolatry) as much as any. He was indeed honest, and of an open and free nature: he had an excellent fancy, brave notions, and gentle expressions. . . . (*Timber or Discoveries*, c. 1623–30)

The reader of Shakespeare's plays is aided by a general knowledge of the way in which they were staged. The King's Men acquired a roofed and artificially lighted theatre only toward the close of Shakespeare's career, and then only for winter use. Nearly all his plays were designed for performance in such structures as the Globe – a three-tiered amphitheatre with a large rectangular platform extending to the center of its yard. The plays were staged by daylight, by large casts brilliantly costumed, but with only a minimum of properties, without scenery, and quite possibly without intermissions. There was a rear stage balcony for action "above," and a curtained rear recess for "discoveries" and other special effects, but by far the major portion of any play was enacted upon the projecting platform, with episode following episode in swift succession, and with shifts of time and place signaled the audience only by the momentary clearing of the stage between the episodes. Information about the identity of the characters and, when necessary, about the time and place of the action was incorporated in the dialogue. No additional indications of place have been inserted in the present editions; these are apt to obscure the original fluidity of structure, with the emphasis upon action and speech rather than scenic background. The acting, including that of the youthful apprentices to the profession who performed the parts of women, was highly skillful, with a premium placed upon grace of gesture and beauty of diction. The audiences, a cross section of the general public, commonly numbered a thousand, sometimes more than two thousand. Judged by the type of plays they applauded, these audiences were not only large but also perceptive.

THE TEXTS OF THE PLAYS

About half of Shakespeare's plays appeared in print for the first time in the folio volume of 1623. The others had been published individually, usually in quarto volumes, during his lifetime or in the six years following his death. The copy used by the printers of the quartos varied greatly in merit, sometimes representing Shakespeare's true text, sometimes only a debased version of that text. The copy used by the printers of the folio also varied in merit, but was chosen with care. Since it consisted of the best available manuscripts, or the more acceptable quartos (although frequently in editions other than the first), or of quartos corrected by reference to manuscripts, we have good or reasonably good texts of most of the thirty-seven plays.

In the present series, the plays have been newly edited from quarto or folio texts depending, when a choice offered, upon which is now regarded by bibliographical specialists as the more authoritative. The ideal has been to reproduce the chosen texts with as few alterations as possible, beyond occasional relineation, expansion of abbreviations, and modernization of punctuation and spelling. Emendation is held to a minimum, and such material as has been added, in the way of stage directions and lines supplied by an alternative text, has been enclosed in square brackets.

None of the plays printed in Shakespeare's lifetime were divided into acts and scenes, and the inference is that the author's own manuscripts were not so divided. In the folio collection, some of the plays remained undivided, some were divided into acts, and some were divided into acts and scenes. During the eighteenth century all of the plays were divided into acts and scenes, and in the Cambridge edition of the mid-nineteenth century, from which the influential Globe text derived, this division was more or less regularized and the lines were numbered. Many useful works of reference employ the act-scene-line apparatus established by the Globe text.

Since the act-scene division thus established is obviously convenient, but is of very dubious authority so far as Shakespeare's own structural principles are concerned, or the original manner of staging his plays, a problem is presented to modern editors. In the present series the act-scene division of the Globe text is retained marginally, and may be viewed as a reference aid like the line numbering. A printer's ornament marks the points of division when these points have been determined by a cleared stage indicating a shift of time and place in the action of the play, or when no harm results from the editorial assumption that there is such a shift. However, at those points where the established division is clearly misleading – that is, where continuous action has been split up into separate "scenes" – the ornament is omitted and the distortion corrected. This mechanical expedient seemed the best means of combining utility and accuracy.

The General Editor.

INTRODUCTION

Macbeth is the shortest of Shakespeare's tragedies and the simplest in its statement: *Thou shalt not kill.* In the words of Coleridge, it contains "no reasonings of equivocal morality, . . . no sophistry of self-delusion." With eyes wide open to the hideousness of his offense, a brave, imaginative, and morally sensitive man commits a stealthy murder for gain. His victim is his guest, his benefactor, his kinsman, and his king; and to shield himself from detection he incontinently sacrifices the lives and reputation of two innocent underlings. The retribution is as appalling as the crime — his soul's slow death in self-horror, degradation, loneliness, and despair, then his bloody extermination.

Why should such a man do such evil? That we ask the question instead of dismissing the play as an incredible fiction is our tribute to the poet's vision and artistry. The question reshapes itself on our lips, Why is there evil for men to do? and we realize that there can be no answer. The core of *Macbeth* is a religious mystery, its moral clarity a testament of faith. Evil may be recognized, loathed, and combated without being understood: " . . . in these matters we still have judgment here."

The earliest mention of the play occurs in notes on a performance at the Globe, April 20, 1611, by the spectator Simon Forman, but the style and a few shreds of literary evidence suggest 1605–6 as the period of composition; hence it followed *Hamlet, Othello,* and possibly also *Lear,* those other tragedies in which destruction is wrought by naked evil, not mere domestic or political strife. *Macbeth* differs from the other three in that the evil works through the protagonist as well as upon him. The one with whom we identify is the one who is possessed; this citadel crumbles from within. The supernatural soliciting of the Weird Sisters, the strenuous persuasions of the wife, do not explain Macbeth's guilt. They enhance its power over our imagination by revealing stages in its course and suggesting forces in perilous balance.

In Holinshed's *Chronicle,* from which Shakespeare drew his material, adding to the sins of the semi-legendary Macbeth those of Donwald, slayer of King Duff, the Weird Sisters are "goddesses of destinie" derived from a heathen fatalism. In the play they are Elizabethan witches, their prescriptive powers subtly curtailed; they predict, abet, and symbolize damnation but do not determine it. Any sense that Macbeth is a helpless victim, his crime predestined, his will bound, is canceled as the play proceeds. We may seem to see in the encounter on the heath the very inception of his lethal designs, but we should ask with Banquo,

> Good sir, why do you start and seem to fear
> Things that do sound so fair ?

Nothing in the witches' prophecies would have suggested to an untainted mind that to "be King hereafter" meant to be murderer first. That Macbeth was already tainted would have been apparent to the original audience. In another play of the era, *The Witch of Edmonton,* the black dog appears at her side only when the wish for his presence is wrung from old Mother Sawyer's lips. The stars could influence but could not govern, the devils could come but only upon summons. At some unknown time for some unknown reason Macbeth has corrupted in pride, and has contemplated the sale of his soul as certainly as Faustus. When we later discover through the words of his Lady that plans to murder Duncan had preceded the meeting on the heath, we should not bring charges of inconsistency, speculate about "lost scenes," or complain that we have been tricked.

The prophecies, nevertheless, without explaining or excusing Macbeth's crimes, impress us as mitigation: powerful and wily forces are speeding him on his course. The more earthly influence of his Lady's persuasions impresses us in a similar way. They provide, moreover, an occasion for the display of his aversion for what he is about to do, and convert it, at least in some measure, from utter self-serving into an offering to her. Lady Macbeth's own behavior is not totally alienating. In a perverted way she is doing what all loyal wives are expected to do, urging her husband on to what she deems his good; here, as in the period of danger that follows, she at least is *all for him*. This is one of the marvels of the play, the manner in which this frightful collusion proceeds in an atmosphere of domestic virtue without the effect of irony. If the evil is great it is also limited, even in respect to the malefactors. After the Lady's collapse, her initial ferocity is remembered as something false to her nature, and the solicitude of her wise and kindly physician seems to us not misplaced.

Macbeth himself is as humane in his reflections as he is inhumane in his acts. Like Iago he is a moralizing villain, but his moralizing is not clever aphoristic display. It comes from his heart, sometimes like an echo of ancient folk beliefs,

It will have blood, they say; blood will have blood.
Stones have been known to move and trees to speak;
Augures and understood relations have

17

By maggot-pies and choughs and rooks brought forth
The secret'st man of blood—

sometimes like religious revelation,

> [Duncan's] virtues
> Will plead like angels, trumpet-tongued against
> The deep damnation of his taking-off;
> And pity, like a naked new-born babe
> Striding the blast, or heaven's cherubin horsed
> Upon the sightless couriers of the air,
> Shall blow the horrid deed in every eye
> That tears shall drown the wind.

No voice in literature has sounded with greater sadness:

> I have lived long enough. My way of life
> Is fall'n into the sear, the yellow leaf;
> And that which should accompany old age,
> As honor, love, obedience, troops of friends,
> I must not look to have; but in their stead,
> Curses not loud but deep, mouth-honor, breath,
> Which the poor heart would fain deny, and dare not.

To say that no one who has become a bloody tyrant would speak in this way is pointless; he would *feel* in this way, or so we are convinced.

By feeling the pangs that we would feel if we were in his place, and by passing our judgments upon himself, Macbeth attaches us to him and consequently himself to us. We cannot view him with cold objectivity as something strange and apart. The unnaturalness of his acts is always counterpoised by the naturalness of his actions: his hesitant overtures to Banquo, his volubility after Duncan's death, his dazed petulance at the appearance of the ghost,

> The time has been
> That, when the brains were out, the man would die,
> And there an end; but now they rise again,
> With twenty mortal murders on their crowns,
> And push us from our stools.

There is something here both grimly humorous and affecting, this killer's speaking in the accents of a hurt child. We should not ascribe Macbeth's humanity to the automatic working of Shakespeare's sympathetic nature. There is nothing casual about it. If Macbeth were other than he is, less like ourselves, he would be a less powerful symbol of our own worst potentialities and the abyss we have escaped. There is nothing of him in Cornwall or Iago for all of Shakespeare's sympathetic nature.

It is hard to believe that so universal a work was calculated to the meridian of any particular person, but there are arguments favoring the possibility. James Stuart, who had ascended the English throne and become the nominal patron of Shakespeare's company a few years before *Macbeth* was written, was supposedly descended from Banquo and was intensely interested in witchcraft; moreover he had assumed in 1605 the prerogative of curing the "king's evil" instituted by Edward the Confessor and mentioned somewhat irrelevantly in the play. On the other hand, one may argue that, had Shakespeare's primary concern been to please the monarch, he might have dramatized more creditable episodes in Scottish history, might have drawn a more flattering portrait of Banquo, and might have seized the opportunity to eulogize the eighth figure in the show of kings (IV, i) since this figure represents James himself. Possibly Shakespeare was responding in his own way to the urgings of his dramatic company; he was in some respects the most reticent writer of his times, and his allusions even to Elizabeth had been few and restrained.

Whether or not *Macbeth* may be considered in a sense "topical" it contains elements that are, or might have been, mere theatrical entertainment. It combines with its great theme the working out of a puzzle, and affords us the pleasure of watching pieces dropping into place. That Macbeth would be king but no father of kings, that he would reign until Birnam Wood marched to Dunsinane, that he would be unconquerable by any man born of woman were riddling prophecies included in Holinshed, but the manner of presenting them through apparitions was Shakespeare's invention: the "Armed Head" instigating the aggression against Macduff probably represents Macbeth himself; the "Child Crowned with a tree in his hand" certainly represents young Malcolm, deviser of the tactics at Birnam Wood; the "Bloody Child" represents Macduff, who was "from his mother's womb Untimely ripped." These ingenuities might well have been intrusive in a play so elemental; as handled by Shakespeare they contribute to the master plan by allowing us to watch Macbeth gradually stripped of hope by those "juggling fiends" upon whom he has relied.

The opportunities for spectacularity offered by the play were seized early, and alterations had already been made in the single version that has come down to us, that printed in the folio of 1623. The Hecate scenes (III, v; IV, i, 39–43, 125–32) are interpolations obviously designed in order to introduce songs and dances by the witches. The first words of the songs, "Come away" and "Black spirits," permit us to identify them as having been borrowed from Thomas Middleton's *The Witch,* where their texts appear in full.

Who wrote the surrounding matter we do not know, but its quality serves one useful purpose. Such lines as

> O, well done! I commend your pains,
> And everyone shall share i' th' gains,
> And now about the cauldron sing
> Like elves and fairies in a ring

make us appreciate the more the magical raucousness of the language that Shakespeare himself gave his witches. The authenticity of the Porter's speech was questioned by Coleridge in one of his critical lapses; this too served a useful purpose, in evoking from De Quincey a gem of literary appreciation. At the Restoration the tradition of spectacular amplification was in full bloom, and on January 7, 1667, Samuel Pepys pronounced a revival as especially excellent "in *divertissement,* though it be a deep tragedy, which is a strange perfection in a tragedy." This "strange perfection" afflicts us still; no other Shakespearean play has provoked more recklessness in the invention of "effects."

Whatever intrudes upon the stark simplicity of this work of art is an offense. It needs no help. Its brevity makes us wonder if there have been cuts as well as additions in the text printed in the folio, but it is hard to imagine any extension that would not have marred its present compact structure. The physical and spiritual terror rises in swift crescendos until Macduff's child is slaughtered at Fife and the universe seems riven in two, then comes the resting place of the scene in England like the still moment at the core of a hurricane; when the blast resumes, it is not to compound chaos but to orchestrate the restoration of moral order. No one who has read the play will ever forget the hardy characters who struggle to readmit light into their murky world, and certainly not that incandescent couple who kill together and die apart. The style has the vigor, condensation, and imaginative splendor of Shakespeare at his greatest, when he seems to be pressing upon the very bounds of the expressible. Blood and darkness are constantly invoked, and jarring antitheses, violent hyperbole, and chaotic imagery give the lines the quality demanded by the action. But there are also moments of unforgettable hush. Some of the speeches seem to express the agony of all mankind:

> Canst thou not minister to a mind diseased,
> Pluck from the memory a rooted sorrow,
> Raze out the written troubles of the brain,
> And with some sweet oblivious antidote
> Cleanse the stuffed bosom of that perilous stuff
> Which weighs upon the heart?

Over the centuries comes the quiet answer, convincing us, as so often the words of this poet so strangely do, that nothing further can be said,

> Therein the patient
> Must minister to himself.

Harvard University ALFRED HARBAGE

Note on the text: The present edition follows closely the only substantive text (folio, 1623), which is mechanically defective but not corrupt in the sense of misrepresenting, in general, Shakespeare's language. The copy was evidently provided by a playhouse manuscript of an acting version. As explained in the general foreword, the act-scene division here supplied marginally is that of the Globe edition. It coincides with the division of the folio text except that V, vii of the latter is subdivided into vii and viii. A more rational point of subdivision comes later (at V, viii, 35) and is marked by some modern editors as scene ix. A stage direction in the folio text indicates that Macbeth was slain in sight of the audience, and this direction is retained in the present text. The body could have been carried "out" by Macduff or another.

The Tragedy of Macbeth

[Names of the Actors

Duncan, *King of Scotland*
Malcolm ⎫
Donalbain ⎭ *his sons*
Macbeth ⎫
Banquo │
Macduff │
Lennox │
Ross ⎬ *noblemen of Scotland*
Menteith │
Angus │
Caithness ⎭
Fleance, *son to Banquo*
Siward, *Earl of Northumberland*
Young Siward, *his son*
Seyton, *an officer attending on Macbeth*
Boy, *son to Macduff*
A Captain
An English Doctor
A Scottish Doctor
A Porter
An Old Man
Three Murderers
Lady Macbeth
Lady Macduff
A Gentlewoman, *attending on Lady Macbeth*
The Weird Sisters
Hecate
The Ghost of Banquo
Apparitions
Lords, Officers, Soldiers, Messengers, Attendants

Scene
Scotland and England]

THE TRAGEDY OF MACBETH

Thunder and lightning. Enter three Witches.   I, i

1. Witch. When shall we three meet again?
  In thunder, lightning, or in rain?
2. Witch. When the hurlyburly's done,
  When the battle's lost and won.
3. Witch. That will be ere the set of sun.   5
1. Witch. Where the place?
2. Witch.   Upon the heath.
3. Witch. There to meet with Macbeth.
1. Witch. I come, Graymalkin!
2. Witch. Paddock calls.
3. Witch.   Anon!
All. Fair is foul, and foul is fair.   10
  Hover through the fog and filthy air.   *Exeunt.*

Alarum within. Enter King [Duncan], Malcolm, Donalbain,   I, ii
  Lennox, with Attendants, meeting a bleeding Captain.

King. What bloody man is that? He can report,

I, i, 8 *Graymalkin* her familiar spirit, a gray cat   9 *Paddock* a toad   *Anon*
at once

25

As seemeth by his plight, of the revolt
The newest state.

Malcolm.   This is the sergeant
Who like a good and hardy soldier fought
5 'Gainst my captivity. Hail, brave friend!
Say to the King the knowledge of the broil
As thou didst leave it.

Captain.   Doubtful it stood,
As two spent swimmers that do cling together
And choke their art. The merciless Macdonwald
10 (Worthy to be a rebel, for to that   p̃me rebel
The multiplying villainies of nature
Do swarm upon him) from the Western Isles
Of kerns and gallowglasses is supplied;
And Fortune, on his damnèd quarrel smiling,
15 Showed like a rebel's whore. But all's too weak:
For brave Macbeth (well he deserves that name),
Disdaining Fortune, with his brandished steel,
Which smoked with bloody execution,
Like valor's minion carved out his passage
20 Till he faced the slave;
Which ne'er shook hands nor bade farewell to him
Till he unseamed him from the nave to th' chops
And fixed his head upon our battlements.

King. O valiant cousin! worthy gentleman!
25 *Captain.* As whence the sun 'gins his reflection
Shipwracking storms and direful thunders break,
So from that spring whence comfort seemed to come
Discomfort swells. Mark, King of Scotland, mark.

I, ii, 3 *sergeant* so designated, apparently, as a staff-officer; he ranks as a
captain 12 *Western Isles* Hebrides (and Ireland?) 13 *kerns* Irish bush-
fighters *gallowglasses* Irish regulars, armored infantrymen 19 *minion*
darling 22 *nave* navel

No sooner justice had, with valor armed,
Compelled these skipping kerns to trust their heels   30
But the Norweyan lord, surveying vantage,
With furbished arms and new supplies of men,
Began a fresh assault.
King.   Dismayed not this
Our captains, Macbeth and Banquo?
Captain.   Yes,
As sparrows eagles, or the hare the lion.   35
If I say sooth, I must report they were
As cannons overcharged with double cracks,
So they doubly redoubled strokes upon the foe.
Except they meant to bathe in reeking wounds,
Or memorize another Golgotha, *Calvary*   40
I cannot tell —
But I am faint; my gashes cry for help.
King. So well thy words become thee as thy wounds,
They smack of honor both. Go get him surgeons.
                              [Exit Captain, attended.]

                    Enter Ross and Angus.

Who comes here?
Malcolm.   The worthy Thane of Ross.   45
Lennox. What a haste looks through his eyes! So should
     he look
That seems to speak things strange.
Ross.   God save the King!
King. Whence cam'st thou, worthy Thane?
Ross.   From Fife, great King,

31 *surveying vantage* seeing opportunity   37 *cracks* explosives   40 *memorize another Golgotha* make memorable as another 'place of the dead'
45 *Thane* a Scottish lord   47 *seems to* seems about to

Where the Norweyan banners flout the sky
50 And fan our people cold.
Norway himself, with terrible numbers,
Assisted by that most disloyal traitor
The Thane of Cawdor, began a dismal conflict,
Till that Bellona's bridegroom, lapped in proof,
55 Confronted him with self-comparisons,
Point against point rebellious, arm 'gainst arm,
Curbing his lavish spirit: and to conclude,
The victory fell on us.

King.   Great happiness!

Ross.   That now
Sweno, the Norways' king, craves composition;
60 Nor would we deign him burial of his men
Till he disbursèd, at Saint Colme's Inch,
Ten thousand dollars to our general use.

King. No more that Thane of Cawdor shall deceive
Our bosom interest. Go pronounce his present death
65 And with his former title greet Macbeth.

Ross. I'll see it done.

King. What he hath lost noble Macbeth hath won. *Exeunt.*

I, iii   *Thunder. Enter the three Witches.*

1. Witch. Where hast thou been, sister?
2. Witch. Killing swine.
3. Witch. Sister, where thou?

53 *dismal* ominous   54 *Bellona* goddess of war   *lapped in proof* clad in
proven armor   55 *self-comparisons* cancelling powers   59 *composition*
terms of surrender   61 *Inch* island   62 *dollars* Spanish or Dutch coins
64 *bosom interest* heart's trust

1. Witch. A sailor's wife had chestnuts in her lap
And mounched and mounched and mounched. 'Give me,'
   quoth I.   5
'Aroint thee, witch!' the rump-fed ronyon cries.
Her husband's to Aleppo gone, master o' th' Tiger:
But in a sieve I'll thither sail
And, like a rat without a tail,
I'll do, I'll do, and I'll do.   10
2. Witch. I'll give thee a wind.
1. Witch. Th' art kind.
3. Witch. And I another.
1. Witch. I myself have all the other,
And the very ports they blow,   15
All the quarters that they know
I' th' shipman's card.
I'll drain him dry as hay.
Sleep shall neither night nor day
Hang upon his penthouse lid.   20
He shall live a man forbid.
Weary sev'nights, nine times nine,
Shall he dwindle, peak, and pine.
Though his bark cannot be lost,
Yet it shall be tempest-tost.   25
Look what I have.
2. Witch. Show me, show me.
1. Witch. Here I have a pilot's thumb,
Wracked as homeward he did come.   *Drum within.*
3. Witch. A drum, a drum!   30
Macbeth doth come.
All. The weird sisters, hand in hand,

I, iii, 6 *Aroint thee* get thee gone   *rump-fed ronyon* fat-rumped scab   15 *very ports they blow* their power to blow ships to ports   17 *card* compass card 20 *penthouse lid* eyelid   21 *forbid* accursed   32 *weird* fate-serving

Posters of the sea and land,
Thus do go about, about,
35   Thrice to thine, and thrice to mine,
And thrice again, to make up nine.
Peace! The charm's wound up.

Enter Macbeth and Banquo.

Macbeth. So foul and fair a day I have not seen.
Banquo. How far is't called to Forres? What are these,
40   So withered and so wild in their attire
That look not like th' inhabitants o' th' earth
And yet are on't? Live you, or are you aught
That man may question? You seem to understand me,
By each at once her choppy finger laying
45   Upon her skinny lips. You should be women,
And yet your beards forbid me to interpret
That you are so.
Macbeth.   Speak, if you can. What are you?
1. Witch. All hail, Macbeth! Hail to thee, Thane of Glamis!
2. Witch. All hail, Macbeth! Hail to thee, Thane of Cawdor!
50   *3. Witch.* All hail, Macbeth, that shalt be King hereafter!
Banquo. Good sir, why do you start and seem to fear
Things that do sound so fair? I' th' name of truth,
Are ye fantastical, or that indeed
Which outwardly ye show? My noble partner
55   You greet with present grace and great prediction
Of noble having and of royal hope,
That he seems rapt withal. To me you speak not.
If you can look into the seeds of time
And say which grain will grow and which will not,

33 *Posters* swift travellers   43 *question* confer with   44 *choppy* chapped
53 *fantastical* creatures of fantasy   55 *grace* honor   57 *rapt withal* spell-
bound at the thought   58 *seeds of time* genesis of events

30

Speak then to me, who neither beg nor fear 60
Your favors nor your hate.
1. Witch. Hail!
2. Witch. Hail!
3. Witch. Hail!
1. Witch. Lesser than Macbeth, and greater. 65
2. Witch. Not so happy, yet much happier.
3. Witch. Thou shalt get kings, though thou be none.
So all hail, Macbeth and Banquo!
1. Witch. Banquo and Macbeth, all hail!
Macbeth. Stay, you imperfect speakers, tell me more: 70
By Sinel's death I know I am Thane of Glamis,
But how of Cawdor? The Thane of Cawdor lives,
A prosperous gentleman; and to be King
Stands not within the prospect of belief,
No more than to be Cawdor. Say from whence 75
You owe this strange intelligence, or why
Upon this blasted heath you stop our way
With such prophetic greeting. Speak, I charge you.
Witches vanish.
Banquo. The earth hath bubbles as the water has,
And these are of them. Whither are they vanished? 80
Macbeth. Into the air, and what seemed corporal melted
As breath into the wind. Would they had stayed.
Banquo. Were such things here as we do speak about?
Or have we eaten on the insane root
That takes the reason prisoner? 85
Macbeth. Your children shall be kings.
Banquo. You shall be King.
Macbeth. And Thane of Cawdor too. Went it not so?
Banquo. To th' selfsame tune and words. Who's here?

66 *happy* fortunate   67 *get* beget   70 *imperfect* incomplete   71 *Sinel* i.e.
Macbeth's father   81 *corporal* corporeal   84 *insane* madness-inducing

Enter Ross and Angus.

    Ross. The King hath happily received, Macbeth,
90   The news of thy success; and when he reads
    Thy personal venture in the rebels' fight,
    His wonders and his praises do contend
    Which should be thine or his. Silenced with that,
    In viewing o'er the rest o' th' selfsame day,
95   He finds thee in the stout Norweyan ranks,
    Nothing afeard of what thyself didst make,
    Strange images of death. As thick as tale
    Came post with post, and every one did bear
    Thy praises in his kingdom's great defense
    And poured them down before him.
100 *Angus.*   We are sent
    To give thee from our royal master thanks;
    Only to herald thee into his sight,
    Not pay thee.
    Ross. And for an earnest of a greater honor,
105   He bade me, from him, call thee Thane of Cawdor;
    In which addition, hail, most worthy Thane,
    For it is thine.
    Banquo.   What, can the devil speak true?
    Macbeth. The Thane of Cawdor lives. Why do you dress me
    In borrowed robes?
    Angus.   Who was the Thane lives yet,
110   But under heavy judgment bears that life
    Which he deserves to lose. Whether he was combined
    With those of Norway, or did line the rebel
    With hidden help and vantage, or that with both

90 *reads* considers 92–93 *His wonders . . . or his* dumbstruck admiration
makes him keep your praises to himself 97 *thick as tale* i.e. as fast as they
can be counted 98 *post with post* messenger after messenger 106 *addition* title 111 *combined* leagued 112 *line* support 113 *vantage* assistance

He labored in his country's wrack, I know not;
But treasons capital, confessed and proved,   115
Have overthrown him.
Macbeth.   [*aside*] Glamis, and Thane of Cawdor —
The greatest is behind! [*to Ross and Angus*] Thanks for
    your pains.
[*Aside to Banquo*] Do you not hope your children shall
    be kings,
When those that gave the Thane of Cawdor to me
Promised no less to them?
Banquo.   [*to Macbeth*] That, trusted home,   120
Might yet enkindle you unto the crown,
Besides the Thane of Cawdor. But 'tis strange:
And oftentimes, to win us to our harm,
The instruments of darkness tell us truths,
Win us with honest trifles, to betray's   125
In deepest consequence. —
Cousins, a word, I pray you.
Macbeth.   [*aside*] Two truths are told,
As happy prologues to the swelling act
Of the imperial theme. — I thank you, gentlemen. —
[*Aside*] This supernatural soliciting   130
Cannot be ill, cannot be good. If ill,
Why hath it given me earnest of success,
Commencing in a truth? I am Thane of Cawdor.
If good, why do I yield to that suggestion
Whose horrid image doth unfix my hair   135
And make my seated heart knock at my ribs
Against the use of nature? Present fears

117 *is behind* is to come 120 *home* all the way 126 *deepest consequence*
i.e. in the vital sequel 127 *Cousins* i.e. fellow lords 128-29 *swelling
act . . . imperial theme* i.e. stately drama of rise to sovereignty 130 *soliciting* inviting, beckoning 136 *seated* fixed 137 *use* way

33

Are less than horrible imaginings.
My thought, whose murder yet is but fantastical,
140   Shakes so my single state of man that function
Is smothered in surmise and nothing is
But what is not.

Banquo.   Look how our partner's rapt.

Macbeth. [aside] If chance will have me King, why chance
    may crown me
Without my stir.

Banquo.   New honors come upon him,
145   Like our strange garments, cleave not to their mould
But with the aid of use.

Macbeth.   [aside] Come what come may,
Time and the hour runs through the roughest day.

Banquo. Worthy Macbeth, we stay upon your leisure.

Macbeth. Give me your favor. My dull brain was wrought
150   With things forgotten. Kind gentlemen, your pains
Are regist'red where every day I turn
The leaf to read them. Let us toward the King.
[Aside to Banquo] Think upon what hath chanced, and at
    more time,
The interim having weighed it, let us speak
Our free hearts each to other.

155 Banquo.   Very gladly.

Macbeth. Till then, enough. – Come, friends.   Exeunt.

139 *fantastical* imaginary 140 *single* unaided, weak *function* normal
powers   142 *rapt* bemused   145 *strange* new   149 *favor* pardon
155 *Our free hearts* our thoughts freely

Flourish. Enter King [Duncan], Lennox, Malcolm, Donal-
    bain, and Attendants.

King. Is execution done on Cawdor? Are not
    Those in commission yet returned?
Malcolm.   My liege,
    They are not yet come back. But I have spoke
    With one that saw him die; who did report
    That very frankly he confessed his treasons,   5
    Implored your Highness' pardon, and set forth
    A deep repentance. Nothing in his life
    Became him like the leaving it. He died
    As one that had been studied in his death
    To throw away the dearest thing he owed   10
    As 'twere a careless trifle.
King.   There's no art
    To find the mind's construction in the face.
    He was a gentleman on whom I built
    An absolute trust.

            Enter Macbeth, Banquo, Ross, and Angus.

                        O worthiest cousin,
    The sin of my ingratitude even now   15
    Was heavy on me. Thou art so far before
    That swiftest wing of recompense is slow
    To overtake thee. Would thou hadst less deserved,
    That the proportion both of thanks and payment
    Might have been mine! Only I have left to say,   20
    More is thy due than more than all can pay.
Macbeth. The service and the loyalty I owe,
    In doing it pays itself. Your Highness' part

I, iv, 2 *in commission* commissioned to carry out the execution 9 *studied*
rehearsed   10 *owed* owned   16 *before* ahead in deserving   19 *proportion*
preponderance

35

Is to receive our duties, and our duties
25 Are to your throne and state children and servants,
Which do but what they should by doing everything
Safe toward your love and honor.

King.   Welcome hither.
I have begun to plant thee and will labor
To make thee full of growing. Noble Banquo,
30 That hast no less deserved nor must be known
No less to have done so, let me enfold thee
And hold thee to my heart.

Banquo.   There if I grow,
The harvest is your own.

King.   My plenteous joys,
Wanton in fullness, seek to hide themselves
35 In drops of sorrow. Sons, kinsmen, thanes,
And you whose places are the nearest, know
We will establish our estate upon
Our eldest, Malcolm, whom we name hereafter
The Prince of Cumberland; which honor must
40 Not unaccompanied invest him only,
But signs of nobleness, like stars, shall shine
On all deservers. From hence to Inverness,
And bind us further to you.

Macbeth. The rest is labor which is not used for you.
45 I'll be myself the harbinger, and make joyful
The hearing of my wife with your approach;
So, humbly take my leave.

King.   My worthy Cawdor!

Macbeth. [aside] The Prince of Cumberland — that is a step
On which I must fall down or else o'erleap,
50 For in my way it lies. Stars, hide your fires;
Let not light see my black and deep desires.

27 *Safe* fitting   28 *plant* nurture   34 *Wanton* unrestrained

The eye wink at the hand; yet let that be
Which the eye fears, when it is done, to see.   *Exit.*
King. True, worthy Banquo: he is full so valiant,
  And in his commendations I am fed;   55
  It is a banquet to me. Let's after him,
  Whose care is gone before to bid us welcome.
  It is a peerless kinsman.   *Flourish. Exeunt.*

Enter Macbeth's Wife, alone, with a letter.   I, v

description of witches

Lady. [*reads*] 'They met me in the day of success; and I have
learned by the perfect'st report they have more in them than
mortal knowledge. When I burned in desire to question them
further, they made themselves air, into which they vanished.
Whiles I stood rapt in the wonder of it, came missives from the 5
King, who all-hailed me Thane of Cawdor, by which title,
before, these weird sisters saluted me, and referred me to the
coming on of time with "Hail, King that shalt be!" This have
I thought good to deliver thee, my dearest partner of greatness,
that thou mightst not lose the dues of rejoicing by being igno- 10
rant of what greatness is promised thee. Lay it to thy heart, and
farewell.'

Glamis thou art, and Cawdor, and shalt be
What thou art promised. Yet do I fear thy nature.
It is too full o' th' milk of human kindness   15
To catch the nearest way. Thou wouldst be great,
Art not without ambition, but without
The illness should attend it. What thou wouldst highly,
That wouldst thou holily; wouldst not play false,

---

52 *wink at the hand* blind itself to what the hand does I, v, 5 *missives*
messengers   18 *illness* ruthlessness

*medeval word for nature
was kind — na ture*

Lady, laborably filled with ambition

And yet wouldst wrongly win. Thou'ldst have, great
20　　Glamis,
That which cries 'Thus thou must do' if thou have it;
And that which rather thou dost fear to do
Than wishest should be undone. Hie thee hither,
That I may pour my spirits in thine ear
And chastise with the valor of my tongue
All that impedes thee from the golden round
Which fate and metaphysical aid doth seem
To have thee crowned withal.

tenderness

　　　　　　　　　　　　　Enter Messenger.

　　　　　　　　　　　　　　What is your tidings?
Messenger. The King comes here to-night.
Lady.　　　　　　　　　　　　Thou'rt mad to say it!
30　Is not thy master with him? who, were 't so,
Would have informed for preparation.
Messenger. So please you, it is true. Our Thane is coming.
One of my fellows had the speed of him,
Who, almost dead for breath, had scarcely more
Than would make up his message.
35　*Lady.*　　　　　　　　　　　Give him tending;
He brings great news.　　　　　　　*Exit Messenger.*
　　　　　　　　　　The raven himself is hoarse
That croaks the fatal entrance of Duncan
Under my battlements. Come, you spirits
That tend on mortal thoughts, unsex me here,
40　And fill me from the crown to the toe top-full
Of direst cruelty. Make thick my blood;
Stop up th' access and passage to remorse,
That no compunctious visitings of nature

26 *round* crown　27 *metaphysical* supernatural　28 *withal* with　34 *breath*
want of breath　39 *mortal* deadly　42 *remorse* pity　43 *nature* natural feeling

38

Shake my fell purpose nor keep peace between
Th' effect and it. Come to my woman's breasts   45
And take my milk for gall, you murd'ring ministers,
Wherever in your sightless substances
You wait on nature's mischief. Come, thick night,
And pall thee in the dunnest smoke of hell,
That my keen knife see not the wound it makes,   50
Nor heaven peep through the blanket of the dark
To cry 'Hold, hold!'

Enter Macbeth.

                    Great Glamis! worthy Cawdor!
Greater than both, by the all-hail hereafter!
Thy letters have transported me beyond
This ignorant present, and I feel now   55
The future in the instant.

Macbeth.   My dearest love,
Duncan comes here to-night.

Lady.   And when goes hence?

Macbeth. To-morrow, as he purposes.

Lady.   O, never
Shall sun that morrow see!
Your face, my Thane, is as a book where men   60
May read strange matters. To beguile the time,
Look like the time; bear welcome in your eye,
Your hand, your tongue; look like th' innocent flower,
But be the serpent under't. He that's coming
Must be provided for; and you shall put   65

44 *fell* fierce   44–45 *keep peace . . . and it* i.e. lull it from achieving its end
46 *for gall* in exchange for gall   *ministers* agents   47 *sightless* invisible
48 *wait on* aid   49 *pall thee* shroud thyself   *dunnest* darkest   55 *ignorant*
i.e. ordinarily unaware   61 *beguile the time* make sly use of the occasion
62 *Look like the time* play up to the occasion

This night's great business into my dispatch,
Which shall to all our nights and days to come
Give solely sovereign sway and masterdom.

Macbeth. We will speak further.

Lady.   Only look up clear.
70 To alter favor ever is to fear.
Leave all the rest to me.   *Exeunt.*

❀

*Hautboys and torches. Enter King [Duncan], Malcolm,
        Donalbain, Banquo, Lennox, Macduff, Ross, Angus,
        and Attendants.*

King. This castle hath a pleasant seat. The air
Nimbly and sweetly recommends itself
Unto our gentle senses.

Banquo.   This guest of summer,
The temple-haunting martlet, does approve
5 By his loved mansionry that the heaven's breath
Smells wooingly here. No jutty, frieze,
Buttress, nor coign of vantage, but this bird
Hath made his pendent bed and procreant cradle.
Where they most breed and haunt, I have observed
The air is delicate.

Enter Lady [Macbeth].

10 *King.*   See, see, our honored hostess!

66 *dispatch* swift management 69 *look up clear* appear untroubled
70 *alter favor* change countenance *fear* incur risk I, vi, S.D. *Hautboys*
oboes 1 *seat* site 3 *gentle* soothed 4 *temple-haunting* nesting in church
spires *martlet* martin, swallow *approve* prove 5 *loved mansionry* beloved nests 6 *jutty* projection 7 *coign of vantage* convenient corner
8 *procreant* breeding

The love that follows us sometime is our trouble,
Which still we thank as love. Herein I teach you
How you shall bid God 'ield us for your pains
And thank us for your trouble.

Lady.   All our service
In every point twice done, and then done double,   15
Were poor and single business to contend
Against those honors deep and broad wherewith
Your Majesty loads our house. For those of old,
And the late dignities heaped up to them,
We rest your hermits.

King.   Where's the Thane of Cawdor?   20
We coursed him at the heels and had a purpose
To be his purveyor; but he rides well,
And his great love, sharp as his spur, hath holp him
To his home before us. Fair and noble hostess,
We are your guest to-night.

Lady.   Your servants ever   25
Have theirs, themselves, and what is theirs, in compt,
To make their audit at your Highness' pleasure,
Still to return your own.

King.   Give me your hand.
Conduct me to mine host: we love him highly
And shall continue our graces towards him.   30
By your leave, hostess.   *Exeunt.*

11–12 *The love . . . as love* the love that sometimes inconveniences us we
still hold precious   13 *God 'ield us* God reward me   20 *hermits* beadsmen
22 *purveyor* advance agent of supplies   26 *Have theirs* have their servants
what is theirs their possessions   *in compt* in trust   28 *Still* always

I, vii   *Hautboys. Torches. Enter a Sewer, and divers Servants with*
        dishes and service over the stage. Then enter Macbeth.

Macbeth. If it were done when 'tis done, then 'twere well
   It were done quickly. If th' assassination
   Could trammel up the consequence and catch
   With his surcease success, that but this blow
5 Might be the be-all and the end-all – ; here,
   But here upon this bank and shoal of time,
   We'ld jump the life to come. But in these cases
   We still have judgment here, that we but teach
   Bloody instructions, which, being taught, return
10 To plague th' inventor. This even-handed justice
   Commends th' ingredience of our poisoned chalice
   To our own lips. He's here in double trust:
   First, as I am his kinsman and his subject,
   Strong both against the deed; then, as his host,
15 Who should against his murderer shut the door,
   Not bear the knife myself. Besides, this Duncan
   Hath borne his faculties so meek, hath been
   So clear in his great office, that his virtues
   Will plead like angels, trumpet-tongued against
20 The deep damnation of his taking-off;
   And pity, like a naked new-born babe
   Striding the blast, or heaven's cherubin horsed
   Upon the sightless couriers of the air,
   Shall blow the horrid deed in every eye
25 That tears shall drown the wind. I have no spur
   To prick the sides of my intent, but only

I, vii, S.D. *Sewer* chief waiter   1 *done* done with   3 *trammel up the conse-*
quence enclose the consequences in a net   4 *his surcease* its (the assassination's) completion   *success* all that follows   7 *jump* risk   9 *instructions*
lessons   17 *faculties* powers   18 *clear* untainted   23 *sightless couriers*
invisible coursers (the winds)

Vaulting ambition, which o'erleaps itself
And falls on th' other —

Enter Lady [Macbeth].

How now? What news?

Lady. He has almost supped. Why have you left the chamber?

Macbeth. Hath he asked for me?

Lady.   Know you not he has?   30

Macbeth. We will proceed no further in this business.
He hath honored me of late, and I have bought
Golden opinions from all sorts of people,
Which would be worn now in their newest gloss,
Not cast aside so soon.

Lady.   Was the hope drunk   35
Wherein you dressed yourself? Hath it slept since?
And wakes it now to look so green and pale
At what it did so freely? From this time
Such I account thy love. Art thou afeard
To be the same in thine own act and valor   40
As thou art in desire? Wouldst thou have that
Which thou esteem'st the ornament of life,
And live a coward in thine own esteem?
Letting 'I dare not' wait upon 'I would,'
Like the poor cat i' th' adage.

Macbeth.   Prithee peace!   45
I dare do all that may become a man;
Who dares do more is none.

Lady.   What beast was't then
That made you break this enterprise to me?
When you durst do it, then you were a man;

---

32 *bought* acquired   37 *green* bilious   45 *cat i' th' adage* (who wants the fish but doesn't want to get its paws wet)   48 *break* broach

43

50 And to be more than what you were, you would
    Be so much more the man. Nor time nor place
    Did then adhere, and yet you would make both.
    They have made themselves, and that their fitness now
    Does unmake you. I have given suck, and know
55 How tender 'tis to love the babe that milks me:
    I would, while it was smiling in my face,
    Have plucked my nipple from his boneless gums
    And dashed the brains out, had I so sworn as you
    Have done to this.

Macbeth.   If we should fail?
Lady.   We fail?
60 But screw your courage to the sticking place
    And we'll not fail. When Duncan is asleep
    (Whereto the rather shall his day's hard journey
    Soundly invite him), his two chamberlains
    Will I with wine and wassail so convince
65 That memory, the warder of the brain,
    Shall be a fume, and the receipt of reason
    A limbeck only. When in swinish sleep
    Their drenchèd natures lie as in a death,
    What cannot you and I perform upon
70 Th' unguarded Duncan? what not put upon
    His spongy officers, who shall bear the guilt
    Of our great quell?

Macbeth.   Bring forth men-children only;
    For thy undaunted mettle should compose
    Nothing but males. Will it not be received,
75 When we have marked with blood those sleepy two

52 *adhere* lend themselves to the occasion 53 *that their fitness* their very
fitness 60 *sticking place* notch (holding the string of a crossbow cranked
taut for shooting) 64 *convince* overcome 66 *receipt* container 67 *lim-
beck* cap of a still (to which the fumes rise) 72 *quell* killing 73 *mettle*
vital substance

Of his own chamber and used their very daggers,
That they have done't?
Lady.   Who dares receive it other,
As we shall make our griefs and clamor roar
Upon his death?
Macbeth.   I am settled and bend up
Each corporal agent to this terrible feat.   80
Away, and mock the time with fairest show;
False face must hide what the false heart doth know.

             Exeunt.

 Enter Banquo, and Fleance, with a torch before him.   II, i

Banquo. How goes the night, boy?
Fleance. The moon is down; I have not heard the clock.
Banquo. And she goes down at twelve.
Fleance.   I take't, 'tis later, sir.
Banquo. Hold, take my sword. There's husbandry in heaven;
Their candles are all out. Take thee that too.   5
A heavy summons lies like lead upon me,
And yet I would not sleep. Merciful powers,
Restrain in me the cursèd thoughts that nature
Gives way to in repose.

  Enter Macbeth, and a Servant with a torch.

    Give me my sword!
Who's there?   10
Macbeth. A friend.

77 *other* otherwise 81 *mock* delude II, i, 4 *husbandry* economy 6 *sum-mons* signal to sleep

Banquo. What, sir, not yet at rest? The King's abed.
    He hath been in unusual pleasure and
    Sent forth great largess to your offices.
15   This diamond he greets your wife withal
    By the name of most kind hostess, and shut up
    In measureless content.
Macbeth.   Being unprepared,
    Our will became the servant to defect,
    Which else should free have wrought.
Banquo.   All's well.
20   I dreamt last night of the three weird sisters.
    To you they have showed some truth.
Macbeth.   I think not of them.
    Yet when we can entreat an hour to serve,
    We would spend it in some words upon that business,
    If you would grant the time.
Banquo.   At your kind'st leisure.
25 *Macbeth.* If you shall cleave to my consent, when 'tis,
    It shall make honor for you.
Banquo.   So I lose none
    In seeking to augment it, but still keep
    My bosom franchised and allegiance clear,
    I shall be counselled.
Macbeth.   Good repose the while.
30 *Banquo.* Thanks, sir. The like to you.
                      Exeunt Banquo [and Fleance].
Macbeth. Go bid thy mistress, when my drink is ready,
    She strike upon the bell. Get thee to bed.
                      Exit [Servant].

---

14 *largess to your offices* gratuities to your household departments   16 *shut up* concluded   18 *will* good will   *defect* deficient means   25 *cleave . . . when 'tis* favor my cause at the proper time   28 *franchised* free from guilt
29 *counselled* open to persuasion

Is this a dagger which I see before me,
The handle toward my hand? Come, let me clutch thee!
I have thee not, and yet I see thee still. 35
Art thou not, fatal vision, sensible
To feeling as to sight? or art thou but
A dagger of the mind, a false creation
Proceeding from the heat-oppressèd brain?
I see thee yet, in form as palpable 40
As this which now I draw.
Thou marshall'st me the way that I was going,
And such an instrument I was to use.
Mine eyes are made the fools o' th' other senses,
Or else worth all the rest. I see thee still, 45
And on thy blade and dudgeon gouts of blood,
Which was not so before. There's no such thing.
It is the bloody business which informs
Thus to mine eyes. Now o'er the one half-world
Nature seems dead, and wicked dreams abuse 50
The curtained sleep. Witchcraft celebrates
Pale Hecate's offerings; and withered murder,
Alarumed by his sentinel, the wolf,
Whose howl's his watch, thus with his stealthy pace,
With Tarquin's ravishing strides, towards his design 55
Moves like a ghost. Thou sure and firm-set earth,
Hear not my steps which way they walk, for fear
Thy very stones prate of my whereabout
And take the present horror from the time,
Which now suits with it. Whiles I threat, he lives; 60

46 *dudgeon* wooden hilt *gouts* blobs 48 *informs* creates impressions
50 *abuse* deceive 52 *Hecate's offerings* worship of Hecate (goddess of
sorcery) 53 *Alarumed* given the signal 55 *Tarquin* Roman tyrant, rav-
isher of Lucrece 59–60 *take . . . suits with it* delay, by prating, the commission of the deed at this suitably horrible moment (?) or, reduce, by
breaking the silence, the suitable horror of this moment (?)

trepidation

Words to the heat of deeds too cold breath gives.

A bell rings.

I go, and it is done. The bell invites me.
Hear it not, Duncan, for it is a knell
That summons thee to heaven, or to hell.   *Exit.*

Enter Lady [Macbeth].

Lady. That which hath made them drunk hath made me
    bold;
    What hath quenched them hath given me fire. Hark!
        Peace!
    It was the owl that shrieked, the fatal bellman
    Which gives the stern'st good-night. He is about it.
5   The doors are open, and the surfeited grooms
    Do mock their charge with snores. I have drugged their
        possets,
    That death and nature do contend about them
    Whether they live or die.
Macbeth.   *[within]* Who's there? What, ho?
Lady. Alack, I am afraid they have awaked,
10 And 'tis not done! Th' attempt, and not the deed,
    Confounds us. Hark! I laid their daggers ready –
    He could not miss 'em. Had he not resembled
    My father as he slept, I had done't.

                        Enter Macbeth.

                                    My husband!
Macbeth. I have done the deed. Didst thou not hear a noise?
15 *Lady.* I heard the owl scream and the crickets cry.
    Did not you speak?
Macbeth.   When?

II, ii, 3–4 *fatal bellman . . . good-night* i.e. like the night-watch cry to felons
scheduled for execution in the morning   6 *possets* bedtime drinks

Lady.   Now.
Macbeth.   As I descended?
Lady. Ay.
Macbeth. Hark!
  Who lies i' th' second chamber?
Lady.   Donalbain.
Macbeth. This is a sorry sight.   20
Lady. A foolish thought, to say a sorry sight.
Macbeth. There's one did laugh in's sleep, and one cried
    'Murder!'
  That they did wake each other. I stood and heard them.
  But they did say their prayers and addressed them
  Again to sleep.
Lady.   There are two lodged together.   25
Macbeth. One cried 'God bless us!' and 'Amen!' the other,
  As they had seen me with these hangman's hands,
  List'ning their fear. I could not say 'Amen!'
  When they did say 'God bless us!'
Lady.   Consider it not so deeply.
Macbeth. But wherefore could not I pronounce 'Amen'?   30
  I had most need of blessing, and 'Amen'
  Stuck in my throat.
Lady.   These deeds must not be thought
  After these ways; so, it will make us mad.
Macbeth. Methought I heard a voice cry 'Sleep no more!
  Macbeth does murder sleep' – the innocent sleep,   35
  Sleep that knits up the ravelled sleave of care,
  The death of each day's life, sore labor's bath,
  Balm of hurt minds, great nature's second course,
  Chief nourisher in life's feast.

27 *hangman's hands* i.e. bloody, like an executioner's   36 *knits up . . .
sleave* smooths out the tangled skein   38 *second course* i.e. sleep, after
food

49

Lady.   What do you mean?

40 *Macbeth.* Still it cried 'Sleep no more!' to all the house;
'Glamis hath murdered sleep, and therefore Cawdor
Shall sleep no more, Macbeth shall sleep no more.'

Lady. Who was it that thus cried? Why, worthy Thane,
You do unbend your noble strength to think

45 So brainsickly of things. Go get some water
And wash this filthy witness from your hand.
Why did you bring these daggers from the place?
They must lie there: go carry them and smear
The sleepy grooms with blood.

Macbeth.   I'll go no more.

50 I am afraid to think what I have done;
Look on't again I dare not.

Lady.   Infirm of purpose!
Give me the daggers. The sleeping and the dead
Are but as pictures. 'Tis the eye of childhood
That fears a painted devil. If he do bleed,

55 I'll gild the faces of the grooms withal,
For it must seem their guilt.   *Exit. Knock within.*

Macbeth.   Whence is that knocking?
How is't with me when every noise appals me?
What hands are here? Ha! they pluck out mine eyes.
Will all great Neptune's ocean wash this blood

60 Clean from my hand? No, this my hand will rather
The multitudinous seas incarnadine,
Making the green one red.

Enter Lady [Macbeth].

Lady. My hands are of your color, but I shame
To wear a heart so white. (*Knock.*) I hear a knocking

44 *unbend* relax   46 *witness* evidence   53 *as pictures* like pictures (since
without motion)   55 *gild* paint   61 *incarnadine* redden   62 *one* uniformly

At the south entry. Retire we to our chamber.   65
A little water clears us of this deed.
How easy is it then! Your constancy
Hath left you unattended. (*Knock*.) Hark! more knocking.
Get on your nightgown, lest occasion call us
And show us to be watchers. Be not lost   70
So poorly in your thoughts.
Macbeth. To know my deed, 'twere best not know myself.
                                                          Knock.
Wake Duncan with thy knocking! I would thou couldst.
                                                          Exeunt.

Enter a Porter. Knocking within.   II, iii

Porter. Here's a knocking indeed! If a man were porter of
hell gate, he should have old turning the key. (*Knock*.)
Knock, knock, knock. Who's there, i' th' name of Belze-
bub? Here's a farmer that hanged himself on th' expectation of plenty. Come in time! Have napkins enow about 5
you; here you'll sweat for't. (*Knock*.) Knock, knock.
Who's there, in th' other devil's name? Faith, here's an
equivocator, that could swear in both the scales against
either scale; who committed treason enough for God's
sake, yet could not equivocate to heaven. O come in, 10
equivocator. (*Knock*.) Knock, knock, knock. Who's
there? Faith, here's an English tailor come hither for steal-
ing out of a French hose. Come in, tailor. Here you may
roast your goose. (*Knock*.) Knock, knock. Never at quiet!
What are you? — But this place is too cold for hell. I'll 15

68 *unattended* deserted   69 *nightgown* dressing-gown   70 *watchers* i.e.
awake   71 *poorly* weakly   II, iii, 2 *old* much   4 *farmer* i.e. one who has
hoarded crops   4–5 *expectation of plenty* prospect of a crop surplus (which
will lower prices)   5 *enow* enough   8 *equivocator* (usually considered an
allusion to the Jesuits tried for political conspiracy)   13 *French hose* close-
fitting breeches   14 *roast your goose* heat your pressing-iron

devil-porter it no further. I had thought to have let in
some of all professions that go the primrose way to th'
everlasting bonfire. (*Knock.*) Anon, anon! *[Opens the
way.]* I pray you remember the porter.

Enter Macduff and Lennox.

20 *Macduff.* Was it so late, friend, ere you went to bed,
     That you do lie so late?
   Porter. Faith, sir, we were carousing till the second cock;
     and drink, sir, is a great provoker of three things.
   Macduff. What three things does drink especially provoke?
25 *Porter.* Marry, sir, nose-painting, sleep, and urine. Lechery,
     sir, it provokes, and unprovokes: it provokes the desire,
     but it takes away the performance. Therefore much drink
     may be said to be an equivocator with lechery: it makes
     him, and it mars him; it sets him on, and it takes him off;
30   it persuades him, and disheartens him; makes him stand
     to, and not stand to; in conclusion, equivocates him in a
     sleep, and, giving him the lie, leaves him.
   Macduff. I believe drink gave thee the lie last night.
   Porter. That it did, sir, i' the very throat on me; but I re-
35   quited him for his lie; and, I think, being too strong for
     him, though he took up my legs sometime, yet I made a
     shift to cast him.
   Macduff. Is thy master stirring?

Enter Macbeth.

   Our knocking has awaked him: here he comes.
   Lennox. Good morrow, noble sir.
40 *Macbeth.*   Good morrow, both.

22 *second cock* second cock-crow (3 a.m.)   30–31 *stand to* stand his guard
33 *gave thee the lie* called you a liar (i.e. unable to stand)   37 *cast*
throw

Macduff. Is the King stirring, worthy Thane?
Macbeth.   Not yet.
Macduff. He did command me to call timely on him;
  I have almost slipped the hour.
Macbeth.   I'll bring you to him.
Macduff. I know this is a joyful trouble to you;
  But yet 'tis one.   45
Macbeth. The labor we delight in physics pain.
  This is the door.
Macduff.   I'll make so bold to call,
  For 'tis my limited service.   *Exit Macduff.*
Lennox. Goes the King hence to-day?
Macbeth.   He does; he did appoint so.
Lennox. The night has been unruly. Where we lay,   50
  Our chimneys were blown down; and, as they say,
  Lamentings heard i' th' air, strange screams of death,
  And prophesying, with accents terrible,
  Of dire combustion and confused events
  New hatched to th' woeful time. The obscure bird   55
  Clamored the livelong night. Some say the earth
  Was feverous and did shake.
Macbeth.   'Twas a rough night.
Lennox. My young remembrance cannot parallel
  A fellow to it.

Enter Macduff.

Macduff. O horror, horror, horror! Tongue nor heart   60
  Cannot conceive nor name thee!
Macbeth and Lennox.   What's the matter?
Macduff. Confusion now hath made his masterpiece:

42 *timely* early   43 *slipped* let slip   46 *physics pain* cures trouble   48 *lim-ited* appointed   54 *combustion* tumult   55 *obscure bird* i.e. the owl   62 *Con-fusion* destruction

Most sacrilegious murder hath broke ope
The Lord's anointed temple and stole thence
The life o' th' building!

65 *Macbeth.*   What is't you say? the life?
Lennox. Mean you his Majesty?
Macduff. Approach the chamber and destroy your sight
With a new Gorgon. Do not bid me speak.
See, and then speak yourselves.

Exeunt Macbeth and Lennox.
Awake, awake!

70 Ring the alarum bell! Murder and treason!
Banquo and Donalbain! Malcolm, awake!
Shake off this downy sleep, death's counterfeit,
And look on death itself. Up, up, and see
The great doom's image. Malcolm! Banquo!

75 As from your graves rise up and walk like sprites
To countenance this horror. Ring the bell!   *Bell rings.*

Enter Lady [Macbeth].

Lady. What's the business,
That such a hideous trumpet calls to parley
The sleepers of the house? Speak, speak!
Macduff.   O gentle lady,
80 'Tis not for you to hear what I can speak:
The repetition in a woman's ear
Would murder as it fell.

Enter Banquo.

O Banquo, Banquo,
Our royal master's murdered!

68 *a new Gorgon* a new Medusa (capable of turning the beholder's eyes to
stone)   74 *great doom's image* a resemblance of the day of judgment
76 *countenance* appear in keeping with   81 *repetition* recital

54

Lady.   Woe, alas!
  What, in our house?
Banquo.   Too cruel anywhere.
  Dear Duff, I prithee contradict thyself   85
  And say it is not so.

              Enter Macbeth, Lennox, and Ross.

Macbeth. Had I but died an hour before this chance,
  I had lived a blessèd time; for from this instant
  There's nothing serious in mortality:
  All is but toys. Renown and grace is dead,   90
  The wine of life is drawn, and the mere lees
  Is left this vault to brag of.

              Enter Malcolm and Donalbain.

Donalbain. What is amiss?
Macbeth.   You are, and do not know't.
  The spring, the head, the fountain of your blood
  Is stopped, the very source of it is stopped.   95
Macduff. Your royal father's murdered.
Malcolm.   O, by whom?
Lennox. Those of his chamber, as it seemed, had done't.
  Their hands and faces were all badged with blood;
  So were their daggers, which unwiped we found
  Upon their pillows. They stared and were distracted.   100
  No man's life was to be trusted with them.
Macbeth. O, yet I do repent me of my fury
  That I did kill them.
Macduff.   Wherefore did you so?
Macbeth. Who can be wise, amazed, temp'rate and furious,
  Loyal and neutral, in a moment? No man.   105

89 *serious in mortality* worthwhile in human life   90 *toys* trifles   91 *lees*
dregs   92 *vault* wine-vault   98 *badged* marked   104 *amazed* confused

The expedition of my violent love
Outrun the pauser, reason. Here lay Duncan,
His silver skin laced with his golden blood;
And his gashed stabs looked like a breach in nature
110 For ruin's wasteful entrance: there, the murderers,
Steeped in the colors of their trade, their daggers
Unmannerly breeched with gore. Who could refrain
That had a heart to love, and in that heart
Courage to make's love known?

Lady.   Help me hence, ho!

Macduff. Look to the lady.

115 *Malcolm. [aside to Donalbain]* Why do we hold our tongues,
That most may claim this argument for ours?

Donalbain. [to Malcolm] What should be spoken here,
Where our fate, hid in an auger hole,
May rush and seize us? Let's away:
Our tears are not yet brewed.

120 *Malcolm.*   *[to Donalbain]* Nor our strong sorrow
Upon the foot of motion.

Banquo.   Look to the lady.
                              [Lady Macbeth is carried out.]
And when we have our naked frailties hid,
That suffer in exposure, let us meet
And question this most bloody piece of work,
125 To know it further. Fears and scruples shake us.
In the great hand of God I stand, and thence
Against the undivulged pretense I fight
Of treasonous malice.

---

106 *expedition* haste   112 *Unmannerly . . . gore* crudely wearing breeches
of blood   *refrain* restrain oneself   115 *Look to* look after   116 *argument
for ours* topic as chiefly our concern   118 *auger hole* i.e. any tiny cranny
121 *Upon the foot of motion* yet in motion   122 *frailties hid* bodies clothed
124 *question* discuss   125 *scruples* doubts   127 *undivulged pretense* secret
stratagems

Macduff. And so do I.

All. So all.

Macbeth. Let's briefly put on manly readiness
  And meet i' th' hall together.

All. Well contented. 130

  Exeunt [all but Malcolm and Donalbain].

Malcolm. What will you do? Let's not consort with them.
  To show an unfelt sorrow is an office
  Which the false man does easy. I'll to England.

Donalbain. To Ireland I. Our separated fortune
  Shall keep us both the safer. Where we are, 135
  There's daggers in men's smiles; the near in blood,
  The nearer bloody.

Malcolm. This murderous shaft that's shot
  Hath not yet lighted, and our safest way
  Is to avoid the aim. Therefore to horse,
  And let us not be dainty of leave-taking 140
  But shift away. There's warrant in that theft
  Which steals itself when there's no mercy left. *Exeunt.*

  Enter Ross with an Old Man. II, iv

Old Man. Threescore and ten I can remember well;
  Within the volume of which time I have seen
  Hours dreadful and things strange, but this sore night
  Hath trifled former knowings.

Ross. Ha, good father,
  Thou seest the heavens, as troubled with man's act, 5
  Threatens his bloody stage. By th' clock 'tis day,

136 *near* nearer   141 *warrant* justification   II, iv, 4 *trifled former knowings*
made former experiences seem trifling   5 *man's act* the human drama

And yet dark night strangles the travelling lamp.
Is't night's predominance, or the day's shame,
That darkness does the face of earth entomb
When living light should kiss it?

10 *Old Man.*   'Tis unnatural,
Even like the deed that's done. On Tuesday last
A falcon, tow'ring in her pride of place,
Was by a mousing owl hawked at and killed.

Ross. And Duncan's horses (a thing most strange and cer-
        tain),

15 Beauteous and swift, the minions of their race,
Turned wild in nature, broke their stalls, flung out,
Contending 'gainst obedience, as they would make
War with mankind.

Old Man.   'Tis said they eat each other.

Ross. They did so, to th' amazement of mine eyes
That looked upon't.

Enter Macduff.

20   Here comes the good Macduff.
How goes the world, sir, now?

Macduff.   Why, see you not?

Ross. Is't known who did this more than bloody deed?

Macduff. Those that Macbeth hath slain.

Ross.   Alas the day,
What good could they pretend?

Macduff.   They were suborned.

25 Malcolm and Donalbain, the King's two sons,
Are stol'n away and fled, which puts upon them
Suspicion of the deed.

7 *travelling lamp* i.e. of Phoebus, the sun   8 *predominance* supernatural as-
cendancy   12 *tow'ring* soaring   13 *mousing* i.e. ordinarily preying on
mice   *hawked at* swooped upon   14 *certain* significant   15 *minions*
darlings   16 *flung out* lunged about   18 *eat* ate   24 *pretend* expect
suborned bribed

Ross.   'Gainst nature still.
  Thriftless ambition, that will raven up
  Thine own live's means! Then 'tis most like
  The sovereignty will fall upon Macbeth.   30
Macduff. He is already named, and gone to Scone
  To be invested.
Ross.   Where is Duncan's body?
Macduff. Carried to Colmekill,
  The sacred storehouse of his predecessors
  And guardian of their bones.
Ross.   Will you to Scone?   35
Macduff. No, cousin, I'll to Fife.
Ross.   Well, I will thither.
Macduff. Well, may you see things well done there. Adieu,
  Lest our old robes sit easier than our new!
Ross. Farewell, father.
Old Man. God's benison go with you, and with those   40
  That would make good of bad, and friends of foes.

                                    Exeunt omnes.

Enter Banquo.   III, i

Banquo. Thou hast it now — King, Cawdor, Glamis, all,
  As the weird women promised; and I fear
  Thou played'st most foully for't. Yet it was said
  It should not stand in thy posterity,
  But that myself should be the root and father   5
  Of many kings. If there come truth from them
  (As upon thee, Macbeth, their speeches shine),

28 *Thriftless* wasteful *raven up* bolt, swallow   32 *invested* crowned
40 *benison* blessing III, i, 3 *foully* cheatingly   4 *stand* continue as a legacy
7 *shine* are brilliantly substantiated

Why, by the verities on thee made good,
May they not be my oracles as well

10 And set me up in hope? But hush, no more!

Sennet sounded. Enter Macbeth as King, Lady [Macbeth],
  Lennox, Ross, Lords, and Attendants.

Macbeth. Here's our chief guest.
Lady.   If he had been forgotten,
  It had been as a gap in our great feast,
  And all-thing unbecoming.
Macbeth. To-night we hold a solemn supper, sir,
  And I'll request your presence.
15 *Banquo.*   Let your Highness
  Command upon me, to the which my duties
  Are with a most indissoluble tie
  For ever knit.
Macbeth.   Ride you this afternoon?
Banquo. Ay, my good lord.
20 *Macbeth.* We should have else desired your good advice
  (Which still hath been both grave and prosperous)
  In this day's council; but we'll take to-morrow.
  Is't far you ride?
Banquo. As far, my lord, as will fill up the time
25 'Twixt this and supper. Go not my horse the better,
  I must become a borrower of the night
  For a dark hour or twain.
Macbeth.   Fail not our feast.
Banquo. My lord, I will not.

S.D. *Sennet* trumpet salute   13 *all-thing* altogether   14 *solemn* state
21 *still* always *prosperous* profitable   25 *Go not my horse the better* i.e.
unless my horse goes faster than anticipated   26 *borrower of* i.e. borrower
of time from

Macbeth. We hear our bloody cousins are bestowed
  In England and in Ireland, not confessing   30
  Their cruel parricide, filling their hearers
  With strange invention. But of that to-morrow,
  When therewithal we shall have cause of state
  Craving us jointly. Hie you to horse. Adieu,
  Till you return at night. Goes Fleance with you?   35
Banquo. Ay, my good lord. Our time does call upon's.
Macbeth. I wish your horses swift and sure of foot,
  And so I do commend you to their backs.
  Farewell.   *Exit Banquo.*
  Let every man be master of his time   40
  Till seven at night. To make society
  The sweeter welcome, we will keep ourself
  Till supper time alone. While then, God be with you!
                         Exeunt Lords [and others].
  Sirrah, a word with you. Attend those men
  Our pleasure?   45
Servant. They are, my lord, without the palace gate.
Macbeth. Bring them before us.   *Exit Servant.*
  To be thus is nothing, but to be safely thus —
  Our fears in Banquo stick deep,
  And in his royalty of nature reigns that   50
  Which would be feared. 'Tis much he dares;
  And to that dauntless temper of his mind
  He hath a wisdom that doth guide his valor
  To act in safety. There is none but he
  Whose being I do fear; and under him   55
  My genius is rebuked, as it is said

32 *invention* falsehoods   33–34 *cause . . . jointly* state business requiring
our joint attention   43 *While* until   44 *Sirrah* form used in addressing
inferiors *Attend* await   48 *but* unless   49 *in Banquo* about Banquo
stick deep are deeply imbedded in me   51 *would* be deserves to be
56 *genius is rebuked* controlling spirit is daunted

Mark Antony's was by Caesar. He chid the sisters
When first they put the name of King upon me,
And bade them speak to him. Then, prophet-like,
60 They hailed him father to a line of kings.
Upon my head they placed a fruitless crown
And put a barren sceptre in my gripe,
Thence to be wrenched with an unlineal hand,
No son of mine succeeding. If't be so,
65 For Banquo's issue have I filed my mind;
For them the gracious Duncan have I murdered;
Put rancors in the vessel of my peace
Only for them, and mine eternal jewel
Given to the common enemy of man
70 To make them kings — the seeds of Banquo kings.
Rather than so, come, Fate, into the list,
And champion me to th' utterance! Who's there?

Enter Servant and two Murderers.

Now go to the door and stay there till we call.
                                    Exit Servant.
Was it not yesterday we spoke together?
Murderers. It was, so please your Highness.
75 *Macbeth.*   Well then, now
Have you considered of my speeches? Know
That it was he, in the times past, which held you
So under fortune, which you thought had been
Our innocent self. This I made good to you
80 In our last conference, passed in probation with you

---

62 *gripe* grasp   65 *filed* defiled   67 *rancors* bitter enmities   68 *jewel* soul
69 *common enemy of man* i.e. Satan   71 *list* lists, field of combat   72 *champion . . . utterance* engage with me to the death   78 *under fortune* out of
favor with fortune   80 *passed in probation* reviewed the evidence

How you were borne in hand, how crossed; the instru-
    ments;
Who wrought with them; and all things else that might
To half a soul and to a notion crazed
Say 'Thus did Banquo.'

1. Murderer.   You made it known to us.

Macbeth. I did so; and went further, which is now   85
    Our point of second meeting. Do you find
    Your patience so predominant in your nature
    That you can let this go? Are you so gospelled
    To pray for this good man and for his issue,
    Whose heavy hand hath bowed you to the grave   90
    And beggared yours for ever?

1. Murderer.   We are men, my liege.

Macbeth. Ay, in the catalogue ye go for men,
    As hounds and greyhounds, mongrels, spaniels, curs,
    Shoughs, water-rugs, and demi-wolves are clept
    All by the name of dogs. The valued file   95
    Distinguishes the swift, the slow, the subtle,
    The housekeeper, the hunter, every one
    According to the gift which bounteous nature
    Hath in him closed, whereby he does receive
    Particular addition, from the bill   100
    That writes them all alike; and so of men.
    Now, if you have a station in the file,
    Not i' th' worst rank of manhood, say't;
    And I will put that business in your bosoms

81 *borne in hand* manipulated *crossed* thwarted *instruments* agents
83 *half a soul* a halfwit *notion* mind 86 *Our point of* the point of our
88 *gospelled* tamed by gospel precepts 92 *catalogue* inventory, classification 94 *Shoughs* shaggy pet-dogs *water-rugs* long-haired water-dogs
clept named 95 *valued file* classification according to valuable traits
97 *housekeeper* watchdog 99 *closed* invested 100 *addition, from the bill*
distinction, contrary to the listing 104 *in your bosoms* in your trust

Whose execution takes your enemy off,
Grapples you to the heart and love of us,
Who wear our health but sickly in his life,
Which in his death were perfect.

2. Murderer.   I am one, my liege,
Whom the vile blows and buffets of the world
Have so incensed that I am reckless what
I do to spite the world.

1. Murderer.   And I another,
So weary with disasters, tugged with fortune,
That I would set my life on any chance
To mend it or be rid on't.

Macbeth.   Both of you
Know Banquo was your enemy.

Murderers.   True, my lord.

Macbeth. So is he mine, and in such bloody distance
That every minute of his being thrusts
Against my near'st of life; and though I could
With barefaced power sweep him from my sight
And bid my will avouch it, yet I must not,
For certain friends that are both his and mine,
Whose loves I may not drop, but wail his fall
Who I myself struck down. And thence it is
That I to your assistance do make love,
Masking the business from the common eye
For sundry weighty reasons.

2. Murderer.   We shall, my lord,
Perform what you command us.

1. Murderer.   Though our lives —

Macbeth. Your spirits shine through you. Within this hour
     at most

---

113 *set* risk   116 *distance* enmity   118 *near'st of life* vital parts   120 *avouch*
justify   121 *For* because of   122 *wail* I must wail

I will advise you where to plant yourselves,
Acquaint you with the perfect spy o' th' time   130
The moment on't, for't must be done to-night
And something from the palace (always thought
That I require a clearness); and with him,
To leave no rubs nor botches in the work,
Fleance his son, that keeps him company,   135
Whose absence is no less material to me
Than is his father's, must embrace the fate
Of that dark hour. Resolve yourselves apart;
I'll come to you anon.
Murderers.   We are resolved, my lord.
Macbeth. I'll call upon you straight. Abide within.   140
It is concluded. Banquo, thy soul's flight,
If it find heaven, must find it out to-night.   *Exeunt.*

Enter Macbeth's Lady and a Servant.   III, ii

Lady. Is Banquo gone from court?
Servant. Ay, madam, but returns again to-night.
Lady. Say to the King I would attend his leisure
For a few words.
Servant.   Madam, I will.   *Exit.*
Lady.   Naught's had, all's spent,
Where our desire is got without content.   5
'Tis safer to be that which we destroy
Than by destruction dwell in doubtful joy.

130 *with the perfect spy o' th' time* by means of a perfect look-out(?) or,
with precise timing (?)   132 *thought* borne in mind   133 *clearness* alibi
134 *rubs* defects

Enter Macbeth.

How now, my lord? Why do you keep alone,
Of sorriest fancies your companions making,
10 Using those thoughts which should indeed have died
With them they think on? Things without all remedy
Should be without regard. What's done is done.
Macbeth. We have scorched the snake, not killed it.
She'll close and be herself, whilst our poor malice
15 Remains in danger of her former tooth.
But let the frame of things disjoint, both the worlds
     suffer,
Ere we will eat our meal in fear, and sleep
In the affliction of these terrible dreams
That shake us nightly. Better be with the dead,
20 Whom we, to gain our peace, have sent to peace,
Than on the torture of the mind to lie
In restless ecstasy. Duncan is in his grave;
After life's fitful fever he sleeps well.
Treason has done his worst: nor steel nor poison,
25 Malice domestic, foreign levy, nothing,
Can touch him further.
Lady.   Come on.
Gentle my lord, sleek o'er your rugged looks;
Be bright and jovial among your guests to-night.
Macbeth. So shall I, love; and so, I pray, be you.
30 Let your remembrance apply to Banquo;
Present him eminence both with eye and tongue:

III, ii, 9 *sorriest* most contemptible   11 *all remedy* any form of remedy
13 *scorched* slashed   14 *close* heal   *poor malice* feeble opposition   16 *frame
of things disjoint* structure of the universe collapse   *both the worlds* i.e.
heaven and earth   21 *torture* rack   22 *ecstasy* frenzy   25 *Malice domestic*
civil war   30 *remembrance* i.e. awareness of the necessity   31 *Present him
eminence* exalt him

Shake is posterity - reproduction

Unsafe the while, that we must lave
Our honors in these flattering streams
And make our faces vizards to our hearts,
Disguising what they are.
Lady.   You must leave this.   35
Macbeth. O, full of scorpions is my mind, dear wife!
  Thou know'st that Banquo, and his Fleance, lives.
Lady. But in them Nature's copy's not eterne.
Macbeth. There's comfort yet; they are assailable.
  Then be thou jocund. Ere the bat hath flown   40
  His cloistered flight, ere to black Hecate's summons
  The shard-borne beetle with his drowsy hums
  Hath rung night's yawning peal, there shall be done
  A deed of dreadful note.
Lady.   What's to be done?
Macbeth. Be innocent of the knowledge, dearest chuck,   45
  Till thou applaud the deed. Come, seeling night,
  Scarf up the tender eye of pitiful day,
  And with thy bloody and invisible hand
  Cancel and tear to pieces that great bond
  Which keeps me pale. Light thickens, and the crow   50
  Makes wing to th' rooky wood.
  Good things of day begin to droop and drowse,
  Whiles night's black agents to their preys do rouse.
  Thou marvell'st at my words, but hold thee still;
  Things bad begun make strong themselves by ill.   55
  So prithee go with me.   *Exeunt.*

32 *lave* dip   34 *vizards* masks   38 *Nature's copy* Nature's copyhold, lease
on life   42 *shard-borne* borne on scaly wings   46 *seeling* sewing together
the eyelids (from falconry)   47 *Scarf up* blindfold   49 *great bond* i.e.
Banquo's lease on life (with suggestion also of the bond of human feeling)
51 *rooky* harboring rooks

Enter three Murderers.

1. Murderer. But who did bid thee join with us?

3. Murderer.   Macbeth.

2. Murderer. He needs not our mistrust, since he delivers
Our offices and what we have to do
To the direction just.

1. Murderer.   Then stand with us.

5   The west yet glimmers with some streaks of day.
Now spurs the lated traveller apace
To gain the timely inn, and near approaches
The subject of our watch.

3. Murderer.   Hark, I hear horses.

Banquo. (*within*) Give us a light there, ho!

2. Murderer.   Then 'tis he: the rest

10   That are within the note of expectation
Already are i' th' court.

1. Murderer.   His horses go about.

3. Murderer. Almost a mile; but he does usually,
So all men do, from hence to th' palace gate
Make it their walk.

Enter Banquo and Fleance, with a torch.

2. Murderer. A light, a light!

3. Murderer.   'Tis he.

15 *1. Murderer.*   Stand to't.

Banquo. It will be rain to-night.

1. Murderer.   Let it come down!

Banquo. O, treachery! Fly, good Fleance, fly, fly, fly!

[Exit Fleance.]

Thou mayst revenge – O slave!   *[Banquo slain.]*

III, iii, 2 *He needs not our mistrust* i.e. we need not mistrust this man 3 *offices* duties 6 *lated* belated 10 *within the note of expectation* on the list of
those expected (invited)

3. Murderer. Who did strike out the light?
1. Murderer.   Was't not the way?
3. Murderer. There's but one down: the son is fled.   20
2. Murderer. We have lost best half of our affair.
1. Murderer. Well, let's away, and say how much is done.

                                                    Exeunt.

       Banquet prepared. Enter Macbeth, Lady [Macbeth], Ross,   III, iv
          Lennox, Lords, and Attendants.

Macbeth. You know your own degrees — sit down:
    At first and last, the hearty welcome.
Lords. Thanks to your Majesty.
Macbeth. Ourself will mingle with society
    And play the humble host.   5
    Our hostess keeps her state, but in best time
    We will require her welcome.
Lady. Pronounce it for me, sir, to all our friends,
    For my heart speaks they are welcome.

                    Enter First Murderer.

Macbeth. See, they encounter thee with their hearts' thanks. 10
    Both sides are even. Here I'll sit i' th' midst.
    Be large in mirth; anon we'll drink a measure
    The table round.   *[Goes to Murderer.]*
    There's blood upon thy face.
Murderer.   'Tis Banquo's then.

19 *Was't not the way* i.e. was it not the right thing to do   III, iv, 1 *degrees*
relative rank, order of precedence   4 *society* the company   6 *keeps her*
state remains seated in her chair of state   10 *encounter* greet

15 *Macbeth.* 'Tis better thee without than he within.
    Is he dispatched?
Murderer.   My lord, his throat is cut:
    That I did for him.
Macbeth.   Thou art the best o' th' cut-throats.
    Yet he's good that did the like for Fleance:
    If thou didst it, thou art the nonpareil.
20 *Murderer.* Most royal sir, Fleance is scaped.
  Macbeth. [*aside*] Then comes my fit again. I had else been
      perfect;
    Whole as the marble, founded as the rock,
    As broad and general as the casing air.
    But now I am cabined, cribbed, confined, bound in
25   To saucy doubts and fears. — But Banquo's safe?
  Murderer. Ay, my good lord. Safe in a ditch he bides,
    With twenty trenchèd gashes on his head,
    The least a death to nature.
Macbeth.   Thanks for that. —
    [*Aside*] There the grown serpent lies; the worm that's fled
30   Hath nature that in time will venom breed,
    No teeth for th' present. — Get thee gone. To-morrow
    We'll hear ourselves again.   *Exit Murderer.*
Lady.   My royal lord,
    You do not give the cheer. The feast is sold
    That is not often vouched, while 'tis a-making,
35   'Tis given with welcome. To feed were best at home;
    From thence, the sauce to meat is ceremony:
    Meeting were bare without it.

21 *perfect* sound of health   22 *founded* solidly based   23 *broad and general*
unconfined *casing* enveloping   24 *cribbed* boxed in   25 *saucy* insolent
27 *trenchèd* deep, trench-like   29 *worm* serpent   32 *hear ourselves* confer
33 *cheer* tokens of convivial hospitality *sold* i.e. not freely given
34 *vouched* sworn   35 *To feed . . . home* i.e. mere eating is best done at
home   36 *meat* food   37 *bare* barren, pointless

Enter the Ghost of Banquo, and sits in Macbeth's place.

Macbeth.   Sweet remembrancer!
　Now good digestion wait on appetite,
　And health on both!
Lennox.   May't please your Highness sit.
Macbeth. Here had we now our country's honor roofed   40
　Were the gracèd person of our Banquo present —
　Who may I rather challenge for unkindness
　Than pity for mischance!
Ross.   His absence, sir,
　Lays blame upon his promise. Please't your Highness
　To grace us with your royal company?   45
Macbeth. The table's full.
Lennox.   Here is a place reserved, sir.
Macbeth. Where?
Lennox. Here, my good lord. What is't that moves your
　Highness?
Macbeth. Which of you have done this?
Lords.   What, my good lord?
Macbeth. Thou canst not say I did it. Never shake   50
　Thy gory locks at me.
Ross. Gentlemen, rise. His Highness is not well.
Lady. Sit, worthy friends. My lord is often thus,
　And hath been from his youth. Pray you keep seat.
　The fit is momentary; upon a thought   55
　He will again be well. If much you note him,
　You shall offend him and extend his passion.
　Feed, and regard him not. — Are you a man?
Macbeth. Ay, and a bold one, that dare look on that
　Which might appal the devil.

37 *remembrancer* prompter 42 *Who may . . . challenge* whom I hope i
may reprove 57 *extend his passion* prolong his seizure

71

60 *Lady.*   O proper stuff!
     This is the very painting of your fear.
     This is the air-drawn dagger which you said
     Led you to Duncan. O, these flaws and starts
     (Impostors to true fear) would well become
65   A woman's story at a winter's fire,
     Authorized by her grandam. Shame itself!
     Why do you make such faces? When all's done,
     You look but on a stool.
     Macbeth.   Prithee see there!
     Behold! Look! Lo! – How say you?
70   Why, what care I? If thou canst nod, speak too.
     If charnel houses and our graves must send
     Those that we bury back, our monuments
     Shall be the maws of kites.   *[Exit Ghost.]*
     Lady.   What, quite unmanned in folly?
     Macbeth. If I stand here, I saw him.
     Lady.   Fie, for shame!
75   *Macbeth.* Blood hath been shed ere now, i' th' olden time,
     Ere humane statute purged the gentle weal;
     Ay, and since too, murders have been performed
     Too terrible for the ear. The time has been
     That, when the brains were out, the man would die,
80   And there an end. But now they rise again,
     With twenty mortal murders on their crowns,
     And push us from our stools. This is more strange
     Than such a murder is.
     Lady.   My worthy lord,
     Your noble friends do lack you.

62 *air-drawn* fashioned of air   63 *flaws* outbursts   64 *Impostors to true
fear* (i.e. because they are authentic signs of false or unjustified fear)
66 *Authorized* sanctioned   72 *monuments* i.e. our only tombs   73 *maws of
kites* bellies of ravens   76 *purged the gentle weal* i.e. purged the state of
savagery   81 *murders on their crowns* murderous gashes on their heads

Macbeth.   I do forget.
Do not muse at me, my most worthy friends: 85
I have a strange infirmity, which is nothing
To those that know me. Come, love and health to all!
Then I'll sit down. Give me some wine, fill full.

Enter Ghost.

I drink to th' general joy o' th' whole table,
And to our dear friend Banquo, whom we miss.   90
Would he were here! To all, and him, we thirst,
And all to all.
Lords.   Our duties, and the pledge.
Macbeth. Avaunt, and quit my sight! Let the earth hide
  thee!
Thy bones are marrowless, thy blood is cold;
Thou hast no speculation in those eyes   95
Which thou dost glare with!
Lady.   Think of this, good peers,
But as a thing of custom. 'Tis no other.
Only it spoils the pleasure of the time.
Macbeth. What man dare, I dare.
Approach thou like the rugged Russian bear,   100
The armed rhinoceros, or th' Hyrcan tiger;
Take any shape but that, and my firm nerves
Shall never tremble. Or be alive again
And dare me to the desert with thy sword.
If trembling I inhabit then, protest me   105
The baby of a girl. Hence, horrible shadow!
Unreal mock'ry, hence!   [*Exit Ghost.*]

91 *thirst* are eager to drink   92 *all to all* let everyone drink to everyone
95 *speculation* intelligence, power of rational observation   101 *Hyrcan*
from Hyrcania, anciently a region near the Caspian Sea   104 *the desert*
a solitary place   105 *If trembling I inhabit* if I tremble   106 *baby of a girl*
a baby girl

                                   Why, so; being gone,
   I am a man again. Pray you sit still.
   Lady. You have displaced the mirth, broke the good meet-
       ing
   With most admired disorder.
110 *Macbeth.*   Can such things be,
   And overcome us like a summer's cloud
   Without our special wonder? You make me strange
   Even to the disposition that I owe,
   When now I think you can behold such sights
115 And keep the natural ruby of your cheeks
   When mine is blanched with fear.
   Ross.   What sights, my lord?
   Lady. I pray you speak not: he grows worse and worse;
   Question enrages him. At once, good night.
   Stand not upon the order of your going,
   But go at once.
120 *Lennox.*   Good night and better health
   Attend his Majesty.
   Lady.   A kind good night to all.
                                        Exeunt Lords.
   Macbeth. It will have blood, they say: blood will have blood.
   Stones have been known to move and trees to speak;
   Augures and understood relations have
125 By maggot-pies and choughs and rooks brought forth
   The secret'st man of blood. What is the night?
   Lady. Almost at odds with morning, which is which.
   Macbeth. How say'st thou, that Macduff denies his person
   At our great bidding?

110 *admired* wondered at   111 *overcome us* come over us   112-13 *You
make . . . I owe* you oust me from my proper role as a brave man
116 *blanched* made pale   124 *Augures* auguries *relations* utterances
125 *maggot-pies* magpies   *choughs* jackdaws (capable of "utterances," as
are magpies and rooks)

                              74

Lady.   Did you send to him, sir?

Macbeth. I hear it by the way; but I will send.   130
There's not a one of them but in his house
I keep a servant fee'd. I will to-morrow
(And betimes I will) to the weird sisters.
More shall they speak, for now I am bent to know
By the worst means the worst. For mine own good   135
All causes shall give way. I am in blood
Stepped in so far that, should I wade no more,
Returning were as tedious as go o'er.
Strange things I have in head, that will to hand,
Which must be acted ere they may be scanned.   140

Lady. You lack the season of all natures, sleep.

Macbeth. Come, we'll to sleep. My strange and self-abuse
Is the initiate fear that wants hard use.
We are yet but young in deed.   *Exeunt.*

Thunder. Enter the three Witches, meeting Hecate.   III, v

1. Witch. Why, how now, Hecate? You look angerly.

Hecate. Have I not reason, beldams as you are,
Saucy and overbold? How did you dare
To trade and traffic with Macbeth
In riddles and affairs of death;   5
And I, the mistress of your charms,
The close contriver of all harms,
Was never called to bear my part
Or show the glory of our art?

130 *by the way* casually   132 *fee'd* paid to spy   133 *betimes* speedily
134 *bent* inclined, determined   140 *ere they may be scanned* i.e. without
being closely studied   141 *season* seasoning, preservative   142 *self-abuse*
delusion   143 *initiate fear* beginner's fear   *wants hard use* lacks toughening
practice   III, v, 2 *beldams* old crones   7 *close* secret

10 And, which is worse, all you have done
 Hath been but for a wayward son,
 Spiteful and wrathful, who, as others do,
 Loves for his own ends, not for you.
 But make amends now: get you gone
15 And at the pit of Acheron
 Meet me i' th' morning. Thither he
 Will come to know his destiny.
 Your vessels and your spells provide,
 Your charms and everything beside.
20 I am for th' air. This night I'll spend
 Unto a dismal and a fatal end.
 Great business must be wrought ere noon.
 Upon the corner of the moon
 There hangs a vap'rous drop profound;
25 I'll catch it ere it come to ground:
 And that, distilled by magic sleights,
 Shall raise such artificial sprites
 As by the strength of their illusion
 Shall draw him on to his confusion.
30 He shall spurn fate, scorn death, and bear
 His hopes 'bove wisdom, grace, and fear:
 And you all know security
 Is mortals' chiefest enemy.

     Music, and a song.

 Hark! I am called. My little spirit, see,
35 Sits in a foggy cloud and stays for me. *[Exit.]*

  Sing within, 'Come away, come away,' &c.

  1. Witch. Come, let's make haste: she'll soon be back again.
              Exeunt.

15 *Acheron* a river of Hades 24 *profound* weighty 26 *sleights* devices
27 *artificial sprites* spirits created by magic arts 32 *security* over-confidence

Enter Lennox and another Lord.

Lennox. My former speeches have but hit your thoughts,
  Which can interpret farther. Only I say
  Things have been strangely borne. The gracious Duncan
  Was pitied of Macbeth. Marry, he was dead!
  And the right valiant Banquo walked too late;   5
  Whom, you may say (if't please you) Fleance killed,
  For Fleance fled. Men must not walk too late.
  Who cannot want the thought how monstrous
  It was for Malcolm and for Donalbain
  To kill their gracious father? Damnèd fact,   10
  How it did grieve Macbeth! Did he not straight,
  In pious rage, the two delinquents tear
  That were the slaves of drink and thralls of sleep?
  Was not that nobly done? Ay, and wisely too,
  For 'twould have angered any heart alive   15
  To hear the men deny't. So that I say
  He has borne all things well; and I do think
  That, had he Duncan's sons under his key
  (As, an't please heaven, he shall not), they should find
  What 'twere to kill a father. So should Fleance.   20
  But peace! for from broad words, and 'cause he failed
  His presence at the tyrant's feast, I hear
  Macduff lives in disgrace. Sir, can you tell
  Where he bestows himself?
Lord.   The son of Duncan,
  From whom this tyrant holds the due of birth,   25
  Lives in the English court, and is received
  Of the most pious Edward with such grace

III, vi, 1 *My former speeches* what I have just said *hit* matched 2 *interpret farther* draw further conclusions 8 *cannot want the thought* can avoid thinking 10 *fact* deed 13 *thralls* slaves 17 *borne* carried off 19 *an't* if it 21 *from broad words* through plain speaking 25 *due of birth* birthright

That the malevolence of fortune nothing
Takes from his high respect. Thither Macduff

30 Is gone to pray the holy King upon his aid
To wake Northumberland and warlike Siward;
That by the help of these (with Him above
To ratify the work) we may again
Give to our tables meat, sleep to our nights,

35 Free from our feasts and banquets bloody knives,
Do faithful homage and receive free honors –
All which we pine for now. And this report
Hath so exasperate the King that he
Prepares for some attempt of war.

Lennox.   Sent he to Macduff?

40 *Lord.* He did; and with an absolute 'Sir, not I,'
The cloudy messenger turns me his back
And hums, as who should say, 'You'll rue the time
That clogs me with this answer.'

Lennox.   And that well might
Advise him to a caution t' hold what distance

45 His wisdom can provide. Some holy angel
Fly to the court of England and unfold
His message ere he come, that a swift blessing
May soon return to this our suffering country
Under a hand accursed!

Lord.   I'll send my prayers with him.

                                       Exeunt.

29 *his high respect* high respect for him   30 *upon his aid* upon Malcolm's behalf   31 *wake* arouse *Northumberland* (English county bordering Scotland)   36 *free* untainted   41 *cloudy* angry   43 *clogs* encumbers 44–45 *Advise him . . . can provide* warn him to keep at as safe a distance as he can devise

Thunder. Enter the three Witches.

IV, i

1. *Witch.* Thrice the brinded cat hath mewed.
2. *Witch.* Thrice, and once the hedge-pig whined.
3. *Witch.* Harpier cries. — 'Tis time, 'tis time!
1. *Witch.* Round about the cauldron go;
   In the poisoned entrails throw.   5
   Toad, that under cold stone
   Days and nights has thirty-one
   Swelt'red venom, sleeping got,
   Boil thou first i' th' charmèd pot.
All. Double, double, toil and trouble,   10
   Fire burn, and cauldron bubble.
2. *Witch.* Fillet of a fenny snake,
   In the cauldron boil and bake;
   Eye of newt, and toe of frog,
   Wool of bat, and tongue of dog,   15
   Adder's fork, and blindworm's sting,
   Lizard's leg, and howlet's wing—
   For a charm of pow'rful trouble
   Like a hell-broth boil and bubble.
All. Double, double, toil and trouble,   20
   Fire burn, and cauldron bubble.
3. *Witch.* Scale of dragon, tooth of wolf,
   Witch's mummy, maw and gulf
   Of the ravined salt-sea shark,
   Root of hemlock digged i' th' dark,   25
   Liver of blaspheming Jew,
   Gall of goat, and slips of yew

IV, i, 1 *brinded* brindled, striped 3 *Harpier* (name of familiar spirit, suggestive of harpy) 8 *Swelt'red venom, sleeping got* exuded venom formed while sleeping 12 *fenny* swamp 16 *blindworm* a lizard, popularly supposed poisonous 23 *mummy* mummified flesh *maw and gulf* stomach and gullet 24 *ravined* insatiable

79

     Slivered in the moon's eclipse,
     Nose of Turk, and Tartar's lips,
30   Finger of birth-strangled babe
     Ditch-delivered by a drab
     Make the gruel thick and slab.
     Add thereto a tiger's chaudron
     For th' ingredience of our cauldron.

35 *All.* Double, double, toil and trouble,
     Fire burn, and cauldron bubble.

  2. Witch. Cool it with a baboon's blood,
     Then the charm is firm and good.

       Enter Hecate and the other three Witches.

Hecate. O, well done! I commend your pains,
40   And every one shall share i' th' gains.
     And now about the cauldron sing
     Like elves and fairies in a ring,
     Enchanting all that you put in.
       Music and a song, 'Black spirits,' &c.
                [Exeunt Hecate and singers.]

  2. Witch. By the pricking of my thumbs,
45   Something wicked this way comes.
     Open locks,
     Whoever knocks!

            Enter Macbeth.

Macbeth. How now, you secret, black, and midnight hags,
     What is't you do?
All.   A deed without a name.
50 *Macbeth.* I conjure you by that which you profess,
     Howe'er you come to know it, answer me.
     Though you untie the winds and let them fight

31 *drab* harlot   32 *slab* sticky   33 *chaudron* guts

Against the churches, though the yesty waves
Confound and swallow navigation up,
Though bladed corn be lodged and trees blown down,   55
Though castles topple on their warders' heads,
Though palaces and pyramids do slope
Their heads to their foundations, though the treasure
Of nature's germens tumble all together
Even till destruction sicken, answer me   60
To what I ask you.

1. *Witch.*   Speak.
2. *Witch.*   Demand.
3. *Witch.*   We'll answer.
1. *Witch.* Say if th' hadst rather hear it from our mouths
Or from our masters.
Macbeth.   Call 'em. Let me see 'em.
1. *Witch.* Pour in sow's blood, that hath eaten
Her nine farrow; grease that's sweaten   65
From the murderer's gibbet throw
Into the flame.
All.   Come, high or low,
Thyself and office deftly show!

Thunder. First Apparition, an Armed Head.

Macbeth. Tell me, thou unknown power —
1. *Witch.*   He knows thy thought:
Hear his speech, but say thou naught.   70
1. *Apparition.* Macbeth, Macbeth, Macbeth, beware Macduff!
Beware the Thane of Fife! Dismiss me. — Enough.
                                        He descends.

---

53 *yesty* yeasty, foamy   54 *Confound* destroy   55 *bladed corn be lodged* ripe
grain be beaten to earth   57 *slope* incline   59 *nature's germens* seeds of creation   60 *sicken* shall surfeit   65 *nine farrow* litter of nine   68 *office* function

Macbeth. Whate'er thou art, for thy good caution thanks:
    Thou hast harped my fear aright. But one word more —
75 *1. Witch.* He will not be commanded. Here's another,
    More potent than the first.

    Thunder. Second Apparition, a Bloody Child.

2. Apparition. Macbeth, Macbeth, Macbeth —
Macbeth. Had I three ears, I'ld hear thee.
2. Apparition. Be bloody, bold, and resolute! Laugh to scorn
80 The pow'r of man, for none of woman born
    Shall harm Macbeth.   *Descends.*
Macbeth. Then live, Macduff, — what need I fear of thee?
    But yet I'll make assurance double sure
    And take a bond of fate. Thou shalt not live;
85 That I may tell pale-hearted fear it lies
    And sleep in spite of thunder.

    *Thunder. Third Apparition, a Child Crowned, with a tree
        in his hand.*

                                      What is this
    That rises like the issue of a king
    And wears upon his baby-brow the round
    And top of sovereignty?
All.   Listen, but speak not to't.
90 *3. Apparition.* Be lion-mettled, proud, and take no care
    Who chafes, who frets, or where conspirers are!
    Macbeth shall never vanquished be until
    Great Birnam Wood to high Dunsinane Hill
    Shall come against him.   *Descends.*
Macbeth.   That will never be.
95 Who can impress the forest, bid the tree

74 *harped* hit the tune of 84 *take a bond of* secure a guarantee from
88 *round* crown 95 *impress* conscript

82

Unfix his earth-bound root? Sweet bodements, good!
Rebellious dead rise never till the Wood
Of Birnam rise, and our high-placed Macbeth
Shall live the lease of nature, pay his breath
To time and mortal custom. Yet my heart   100
Throbs to know one thing. Tell me, if your art
Can tell so much: Shall Banquo's issue ever
Reign in this kingdom?

All.   Seek to know no more.

Macbeth. I will be satisfied. Deny me this,
And an eternal curse fall on you! Let me know.   105
Why sinks that cauldron? and what noise is this?

Hautboys.

1. Witch. Show!
2. Witch. Show!
3. Witch. Show!
All. Show his eyes, and grieve his heart!   110
Come like shadows, so depart!

*A show of eight Kings and Banquo, last [King] with a
glass in his hand.*

Macbeth. Thou art too like the spirit of Banquo. Down!   .
Thy crown does sear mine eyeballs. And thy hair,
Thou other gold-bound brow, is like the first.
A third is like the former. Filthy hags,   115
Why do you show me this? A fourth? Start, eyes!
What, will the line stretch out to th' crack of doom?
Another yet? A seventh? I'll see no more.
And yet the eighth appears, who bears a glass
Which shows me many more; and some I see   120

96 *bodements* prophecies   99 *lease of nature* i.e. the full lifespan   100 *mortal
custom* normal death   102 *issue* offspring   106 *noise* music   116 *Start*
bulge

That twofold balls and treble sceptres carry.
Horrible sight! Now I see 'tis true;
For the blood-boltered Banquo smiles upon me
And points at them for his. What? Is this so?

125 *1. Witch.* Ay, sir, all this is so. But why
Stands Macbeth thus amazedly?
Come, sisters, cheer we up his sprites
And show the best of our delights.
I'll charm the air to give a sound

130 While you perform your antic round,
That this great king may kindly say
Our duties did his welcome pay.

Music. The Witches dance, and vanish.

Macbeth. Where are they? Gone? Let this pernicious hour
Stand aye accursèd in the calendar!
Come in, without there!

Enter Lennox.

135 *Lennox.*   What's your Grace's will?
Macbeth. Saw you the weird sisters?
Lennox.   No, my lord.
Macbeth. Came they not by you?
Lennox.   No indeed, my lord.
Macbeth. Infected be the air whereon they ride,
And damned all those that trust them! I did hear

140 The galloping of horse. Who was't came by?
Lennox. 'Tis two or three, my lord, that bring you word
Macduff is fled to England.
Macbeth.   Fled to England?
Lennox. Ay, my good lord.

---

121 *twofold balls and treble sceptres* (English coronation insignia)   123 *blood-boltered* matted with blood   127 *sprites* spirits   130 *antic round* grotesque circular dance

Macbeth. *[aside]* Time, thou anticipat'st my dread exploits.
  The flighty purpose never is o'ertook   145
  Unless the deed go with it. From this moment
  The very firstlings of my heart shall be
  The firstlings of my hand. And even now,
  To crown my thoughts with acts, be it thought and done:
  The castle of Macduff I will surprise,   150
  Seize upon Fife, give to th' edge o' th' sword
  His wife, his babes, and all unfortunate souls
  That trace him in his line. No boasting like a fool;
  This deed I'll do before this purpose cool.
  But no more sights! — Where are these gentlemen?   155
  Come, bring me where they are.   *Exeunt.*

Enter Macduff's Wife, her Son, and Ross.   IV, ii

Wife. What had he done to make him fly the land?
Ross. You must have patience, madam.
Wife.   He had none.
  His flight was madness. When our actions do not,
  Our fears do make us traitors.
Ross.   You know not
  Whether it was his wisdom or his fear.   5
Wife. Wisdom? To leave his wife, to leave his babes,
  His mansion and his titles in a place
  From whence himself does fly? He loves us not,
  He wants the natural touch. For the poor wren

---

144 *anticipat'st* forestall 145 *flighty* fleeting 147–48 *firstlings . . . my
hand* i.e. I shall act at the moment I feel the first impulse 153 *trace* follow
line family line   IV, ii, 2 *patience* self-control 4 *traitors* i.e. traitors to ourselves 9 *wants* lacks

10 (The most diminutive of birds) will fight,
    Her young ones in her nest, against the owl.
    All is the fear and nothing is the love,
    As little is the wisdom, where the flight
    So runs against all reason.

Ross.   My dearest coz,

15 I pray you school yourself. But for your husband,
    He is noble, wise, judicious, and best knows
    The fits o' th' season. I dare not speak much further,
    But cruel are the times when we are traitors
    And do not know ourselves; when we hold rumor

20 From what we fear, yet know not what we fear
    But float upon a wild and violent sea
    Each way and none. I take my leave of you.
    Shall not be long but I'll be here again.
    Things at the worst will cease, or else climb upward

25 To what they were before. – My pretty cousin,
    Blessing upon you!

Wife. Fathered he is, and yet he's fatherless.

Ross. I am so much a fool, should I stay longer
    It would be my disgrace and your discomfort.
    I take my leave at once.   *Exit.*

30 *Wife.*   Sirrah, your father's dead;
    And what will you do now? How will you live?

Son. As birds do, mother.

Wife.   What, with worms and flies?

Son. With what I get, I mean; and so do they.

Wife. Poor bird! thou'dst never fear the net nor lime,

35 The pitfall nor the gin.

14 *coz* cousin, kinswoman   17 *fits o' th' season* present disorders   19 *know
ourselves* know ourselves to be so   19–20 *hold rumor . . . we fear* are credu-
lous in accordance with our fears   24 *will cease* i.e. must cease descending
29 *would be my* would be to my (i.e. his weeping)   34 *lime* birdlime
35 *gin* trap

Son. Why should I, mother? Poor birds they are not set for.
  My father is not dead for all your saying.

Wife. Yes, he is dead. How wilt thou do for a father?

Son. Nay, how will you do for a husband?

Wife. Why, I can buy me twenty at any market.   40

Son. Then you'll buy 'em to sell again.

Wife. Thou speak'st with all thy wit; and yet, i' faith,
  With wit enough for thee.

Son. Was my father a traitor, mother?

Wife. Ay, that he was!   45

Son. What is a traitor?

Wife. Why, one that swears and lies.

Son. And be all traitors that do so?

Wife. Every one that does so is a traitor and must be
  hanged.   50

Son. And must they all be hanged that swear and lie?

Wife. Every one.

Son. Who must hang them?

Wife. Why, the honest men.

Son. Then the liars and swearers are fools, for there are liars 55
  and swearers enow to beat the honest men and hang up
  them.

Wife. Now God help thee, poor monkey! But how wilt
  thou do for a father?

Son. If he were dead, you'ld weep for him. If you would 60
  not, it were a good sign that I should quickly have a new
  father.

Wife. Poor prattler, how thou talk'st!

Enter a Messenger.

Messenger. Bless you, fair dame! I am not to you known,

41 *sell* betray   42–43 *Thou speak'st . . . for thee* i.e. you use all the intelligence you have, and it is quite enough   56 *enow* enough

87

65   Though in your state of honor I am perfect.
      I doubt some danger does approach you nearly.
      If you will take a homely man's advice,
      Be not found here. Hence with your little ones!
      To fright you thus methinks I am too savage;
70   To do worse to you were fell cruelty,
      Which is too nigh your person. Heaven preserve you!
      I dare abide no longer.   *Exit.*

Wife.   Whither should I fly?
      I have done no harm. But I remember now
      I am in this earthly world, where to do harm
75   Is often laudable, to do good sometime
      Accounted dangerous folly. Why then, alas,
      Do I put up that womanly defense
      To say I have done no harm? — What are these faces?

                    Enter Murderers.

Murderer. Where is your husband?
80 *Wife.* I hope in no place so unsanctified
      Where such as thou mayst find him.
Murderer.   He's a traitor.
Son. Thou liest, thou shag-eared villain!
Murderer.   What, you egg! *[Stabs him.]*
      Young fry of treachery!
Son.   He has killed me, mother.
      Run away, I pray you!   *[Dies.]*
                    Exit [Wife], crying 'Murder!' [pursued by Murderers].

65 *in your state . . . perfect* I am informed of your noble identity   66 *doubt*
fear   67 *homely* plain   70–71 *To do worse . . . your person* i.e. not to frighten
you were to do worse, expose you to that fierce cruelty which is impending
82 *shag-eared* i.e. with shaggy hair falling about the ears   83 *fry* spawn

Enter Malcolm and Macduff.

Malcolm. Let us seek out some desolate shade, and there
  Weep our sad bosoms empty.
Macduff.   Let us rather
  Hold fast the mortal sword and, like good men,
  Bestride our downfall'n birthdom. Each new morn
  New widows howl, new orphans cry, new sorrows   5
  Strike heaven on the face, that it resounds
  As if it felt with Scotland and yelled out
  Like syllable of dolor.
Malcolm.   What I believe, I'll wail;
  What know, believe; and what I can redress,
  As I shall find the time to friend, I will.   10
  What you have spoke, it may be so perchance.
  This tyrant, whose sole name blisters our tongues,
  Was once thought honest; you have loved him well;
  He hath not touched you yet. I am young; but something
  You may deserve of him through me, and wisdom   15
  To offer up a weak, poor, innocent lamb
  T' appease an angry god.
Macduff. I am not treacherous.
Malcolm.   But Macbeth is.
  A good and virtuous nature may recoil
  In an imperial charge. But I shall crave your pardon.   20
  That which you are, my thoughts cannot transpose:
  Angels are bright still though the brightest fell;
  Though all things foul would wear the brows of grace,
  Yet grace must still look so.

IV, iii, 3 *mortal* deadly 4 *Bestride* i.e. stand over protectively *birthdom*
place of birth 8 *Like syllable of dolor* a similar cry of pain 10 *time to
friend* time propitious 12 *sole name* very name 14 *young* i.e. young and
inexperienced 15 *wisdom* i.e. it may be wise 19–20 *recoil . . . imperial
charge* reverse itself under royal pressure 21 *transpose* alter 22 *the
brightest* i.e. Lucifer

Macduff.   I have lost my hopes.

25 *Malcolm.* Perchance even there where I did find my doubts.
Why in that rawness left you wife and child,
Those precious motives, those strong knots of love,
Without leave-taking? I pray you,
Let not my jealousies be your dishonors,
30 But mine own safeties. You may be rightly just
Whatever I shall think.

Macduff.   Bleed, bleed, poor country!
Great tyranny, lay thou thy basis sure,
For goodness dare not check thee, wear thou thy wrongs,
The title is affeered! Fare thee well, lord.
35 I would not be the villain that thou think'st
For the whole space that's in the tyrant's grasp
And the rich East to boot.

Malcolm.   Be not offended.
I speak not as in absolute fear of you.
I think our country sinks beneath the yoke,
40 It weeps, it bleeds, and each new day a gash
Is added to her wounds. I think withal
There would be hands uplifted in my right;
And here from gracious England have I offer
Of goodly thousands. But, for all this,
45 When I shall tread upon the tyrant's head
Or wear it on my sword, yet my poor country
Shall have more vices than it had before,
More suffer, and more sundry ways than ever,
By him that shall succeed.

Macduff.   What should he be?

50 *Malcolm.* It is myself I mean, in whom I know

26 *rawness* unprotected state   29 *jealousies* suspicions   32 *basis* foundation
34 *affeered* confirmed by law   38 *absolute* complete   41 *withal* further-
more

All the particulars of vice so grafted
That, when they shall be opened, black Macbeth
Will seem as pure as snow, and the poor state
Esteem him as a lamb, being compared
With my confineless harms.

Macduff.   Not in the legions   55
Of horrid hell can come a devil more damned
In evils to top Macbeth.

Malcolm.   I grant him bloody,
Luxurious, avaricious, false, deceitful,
Sudden, malicious, smacking of every sin
That has a name. But there's no bottom, none,   60
In my voluptuousness. Your wives, your daughters,
Your matrons, and your maids could not fill up
The cistern of my lust; and my desire
All continent impediments would o'erbear
That did oppose my will. Better Macbeth   65
Than such an one to reign.

Macduff.   Boundless intemperance
In nature is a tyranny. It hath been
Th' untimely emptying of the happy throne
And fall of many kings. But fear not yet
To take upon you what is yours. You may   70
Convey your pleasures in a spacious plenty
And yet seem cold – the time you may so hoodwink.
We have willing dames enough. There cannot be
That vulture in you to devour so many
As will to greatness dedicate themselves,   75
Finding it so inclined.

---

51 *particulars* varieties *grafted* implanted   52 *opened* revealed   55 *confineless harms* unlimited vices   58 *Luxurious* lecherous   59 *Sudden*
violent   64 *continent* containing, restraining   67 *In nature* in one's nature
71 *Convey* obtain by stealth

Malcolm.   With this there grows
In my most ill-composed affection such
A stanchless avarice that, were I King,
I should cut off the nobles for their lands,
80 Desire his jewels, and this other's house,
And my more-having would be as a sauce
To make me hunger more, that I should forge
Quarrels unjust against the good and loyal,
Destroying them for wealth.

Macduff.   This avarice
85 Sticks deeper, grows with more pernicious root
Than summer-seeming lust, and it hath been
The sword of our slain kings. Yet do not fear.
Scotland hath foisons to fill up your will
Of your mere own. All these are portable,
90 With other graces weighed.

Malcolm. But I have none. The king-becoming graces,
As justice, verity, temp'rance, stableness,
Bounty, perseverance, mercy, lowliness,
Devotion, patience, courage, fortitude,
95 I have no relish of them, but abound
In the division of each several crime,
Acting it many ways. Nay, had I pow'r, I should
Pour the sweet milk of concord into hell,
Uproar the universal peace, confound
All unity on earth.

100 *Macduff.*   O Scotland, Scotland!

Malcolm. If such a one be fit to govern, speak.
I am as I have spoken.

---

77 *ill-composed affection* disordered disposition 78 *stanchless* insatiable
82 *forge* fabricate 86 *summer-seeming* i.e. seasonal, transitory 87 *sword
of our slain* cause of death of our 88–89 *foisons . . . mere own* riches of
your own enough to satisfy you 89 *portable* bearable 93 *lowliness* humility 95 *relish* trace 96 *division* subdivisions 99 *Uproar* blast

Macduff.   Fit to govern?
No, not to live! O nation miserable,
With an untitled tyrant bloody-sceptred,
When shalt thou see thy wholesome days again,   105
Since that the truest issue of thy throne
By his own interdiction stands accursed
And does blaspheme his breed? Thy royal father
Was a most sainted king; the queen that bore thee,
Oft'ner upon her knees than on her feet,   110
Died every day she lived. Fare thee well.
These evils thou repeat'st upon thyself
Hath banished me from Scotland. O my breast,
Thy hope ends here!
Malcolm.   Macduff, this noble passion,
Child of integrity, hath from my soul   115
Wiped the black scruples, reconciled my thoughts
To thy good truth and honor. Devilish Macbeth
By many of these trains hath sought to win me
Into his power; and modest wisdom plucks me
From over-credulous haste; but God above   120
Deal between thee and me, for even now
I put myself to thy direction and
Unspeak mine own detraction, here abjure
The taints and blames I laid upon myself
For strangers to my nature. I am yet   125
Unknown to woman, never was forsworn,
Scarcely have coveted what was mine own,
At no time broke my faith, would not betray
The devil to his fellow, and delight
No less in truth than life. My first false speaking   130

---

107 *interdiction* curse   111 *Died* i.e. turned away from this life   116 *scruples* doubts   118 *trains* plots   119 *modest* cautious   *plucks* holds   125 *For* as

Was this upon myself. What I am truly,
Is thine and my poor country's to command;
Whither indeed, before thy here-approach,
Old Siward with ten thousand warlike men
135   Already at a point was setting forth.
Now we'll together; and the chance of goodness
Be like our warranted quarrel! Why are you silent?
Macduff. Such welcome and unwelcome things at once
'Tis hard to reconcile.

Enter a Doctor.

Malcolm. Well, more anon. Comes the King forth, I pray
140   you?
Doctor. Ay, sir. There are a crew of wretched souls
That stay his cure. Their malady convinces
The great assay of art; but at his touch,
Such sanctity hath heaven given his hand,
They presently amend.
145 *Malcolm.*   I thank you, doctor.

Exit [Doctor].

Macduff. What's the disease he means?
Malcolm.   'Tis called the evil.
A most miraculous work in this good King,
Which often since my here-remain in England
I have seen him do: how he solicits heaven
150   Himself best knows, but strangely-visited people,
All swol'n and ulcerous, pitiful to the eye,
The mere despair of surgery, he cures,

---

131 *upon* against 135 *at a point* armed 136–37 *the chance . . . warranted quarrel* i.e. let the chance of success equal the justice of our cause 140 *anon* soon 142 *stay* await *convinces* baffles 143 *assay of art* resources of medical science 146 *evil* scrofula (king's evil) 150 *strangely-visited* unusually afflicted 152 *mere* utter

Hanging a golden stamp about their necks,
Put on with holy prayers; and 'tis spoken,
To the succeeding royalty he leaves   155
The healing benediction. With this strange virtue,
He hath a heavenly gift of prophecy,
And sundry blessings hang about his throne
That speak him full of grace.

Enter Ross.

Macduff.   See who comes here.
Malcolm. My countryman; but yet I know him not.   160
Macduff. My ever gentle cousin, welcome hither.
Malcolm. I know him now. Good God betimes remove
  The means that makes us strangers!
Ross.   Sir, amen.
Macduff. Stands Scotland where it did?
Ross.   Alas, poor country,
  Almost afraid to know itself. It cannot   165
  Be called our mother but our grave, where nothing
  But who knows nothing is once seen to smile;
  Where sighs and groans, and shrieks that rent the air,
  Are made, not marked; where violent sorrow seems
  A modern ecstasy. The dead man's knell   170
  Is there scarce asked for who, and good men's lives
  Expire before the flowers in their caps,
  Dying or ere they sicken.
Macduff.   O, relation
  Too nice, and yet too true!
Malcolm.   What's the newest grief?

153 *stamp* coin   162 *betimes* quickly   166 *nothing* no one   169 *marked*
noticed   170 *modern ecstasy* commonplace emotion   171 *Is there . . . for
who* scarcely calls forth an inquiry about identity   174 *nice* precise

175 *Ross.* That of an hour's age doth hiss the speaker;
    Each minute teems a new one.

Macduff.   How does my wife?

Ross. Why, well.

Macduff.   And all my children?

Ross.   Well too.

Macduff. The tyrant has not battered at their peace?

Ross. No, they were well at peace when I did leave 'em.

180 *Macduff.* Be not a niggard of your speech. How goes't?

Ross. When I came hither to transport the tidings
    Which I have heavily borne, there ran a rumor
    Of many worthy fellows that were out,
    Which was to my belief witnessed the rather

185   For that I saw the tyrant's power afoot.
    Now is the time of help. Your eye in Scotland
    Would create soldiers, make our women fight
    To doff their dire distresses.

Malcolm.   Be't their comfort
    We are coming thither. Gracious England hath

190   Lent us good Siward and ten thousand men,
    An older and a better soldier none
    That Christendom gives out.

Ross.   Would I could answer
    This comfort with the like. But I have words
    That would be howled out in the desert air,
    Where hearing should not latch them.

195 *Macduff.*   What concern they,
    The general cause or is it a fee-grief
    Due to some single breast?

---

175 *hiss the speaker* causes the speaker to be hissed (for stale repetition)
176 *teems* brings forth 182 *heavily borne* sadly carried 183 *out* up in
arms 184 *witnessed* attested 192 *gives out* reports 195 *latch* catch hold
of 196 *fee-grief* i.e. a grief possessed in private 197 *Due* belonging

Ross.   No mind that's honest
  But in it shares some woe, though the main part
  Pertains to you alone.
Macduff.   If it be mine,
  Keep it not from me, quickly let me have it.   200
Ross. Let not your ears despise my tongue for ever,
  Which shall possess them with the heaviest sound
  That ever yet they heard.
Macduff.   Humh! I guess at it.
Ross. Your castle is surprised, your wife and babes
  Savagely slaughtered. To relate the manner   205
  Were, on the quarry of these murdered deer,
  To add the death of you.
Malcolm.   Merciful heaven!
  What, man! Ne'er pull your hat upon your brows.
  Give sorrow words. The grief that does not speak
  Whispers the o'erfraught heart and bids it break.   210
Macduff. My children too?
Ross.   Wife, children, servants, all
  That could be found.
Macduff.   And I must be from thence?
  My wife killed too?
Ross.   I have said.
Malcolm.   Be comforted.
  Let's make us med'cines of our great revenge
  To cure this deadly grief.   215
Macduff. He has no children. All my pretty ones?
  Did you say all? O hell-kite! All?
  What, all my pretty chickens and their dam
  At one fell swoop?
Malcolm. Dispute it like a man.

204 *surprised* attacked   206 *quarry* heap of game   209 *speak* speak aloud
210 *Whispers* whispers to   220 *Dispute* revenge

97

220 *Macduff.*   I shall do so;
      But I must also feel it as a man.
      I cannot but remember such things were
      That were most precious to me. Did heaven look on
      And would not take their part? Sinful Macduff,
225   They were all struck for thee! Naught that I am,
      Not for their own demerits but for mine
      Fell slaughter on their souls. Heaven rest them now!
Malcolm. Be this the whetstone of your sword. Let grief
      Convert to anger; blunt not the heart, enrage it.
230 *Macduff.* O, I could play the woman with mine eyes
      And braggart with my tongue. But, gentle heavens,
      Cut short all intermission. Front to front
      Bring thou this fiend of Scotland and myself.
      Within my sword's length set him. If he scape,
      Heaven forgive him too!
235 *Malcolm.*   This tune goes manly.
      Come, go we to the King. Our power is ready;
      Our lack is nothing but our leave. Macbeth
      Is ripe for shaking, and the pow'rs above
      Put on their instruments. Receive what cheer you may.
240   The night is long that never finds the day.   *Exeunt.*

V, i   *Enter a Doctor of Physic and a Waiting Gentlewoman.*

      Doctor. I have two nights watched with you, but can per-
        ceive no truth in your report. When was it she last
        walked?

225 *Naught* wicked   232 *intermission* interval   *Front to front* face to face
236 *power* army   237 *Our lack ... our leave* i.e. nothing remains but to say
farewell   239 *Put on their instruments* urge on their agents

Gentlewoman. Since his Majesty went into the field I have
    seen her rise from her bed, throw her nightgown upon 5
    her, unlock her closet, take forth paper, fold it, write
    upon't, read it, afterwards seal it, and again return to bed;
    yet all this while in a most fast sleep.

Doctor. A great perturbation in nature, to receive at once
    the benefit of sleep and do the effects of watching! In this 10
    slumb'ry agitation, besides her walking and other actual
    performances, what (at any time) have you heard her say?

Gentlewoman. That, sir, which I will not report after her.

Doctor. You may to me, and 'tis most meet you should.

Gentlewoman. Neither to you nor any one, having no wit- 15
    ness to confirm my speech.

        Enter Lady [Macbeth], with a taper.

Lo you, here she comes! This is her very guise, and, upon
    my life, fast asleep! Observe her; stand close.

Doctor. How came she by that light?

Gentlewoman. Why, it stood by her. She has light by her 20
    continually. 'Tis her command.

Doctor. You see her eyes are open.

Gentlewoman. Ay, but their sense are shut.

Doctor. What is it she does now? Look how she rubs her
    hands. 25

Gentlewoman. It is an accustomed action with her, to seem
    thus washing her hands. I have known her continue in
    this a quarter of an hour.

Lady. Yet here's a spot.

Doctor. Hark, she speaks. I will set down what comes from 30
    her, to satisfy my remembrance the more strongly.

V, i, 5 *nightgown* dressing-gown 6 *closet* a chest, or desk 10 *do the effects
of watching* act as if awake 14 *meet* fitting 17 *guise* habit 18 *close* con-
cealed 23 *sense* powers of sensation

Lady. Out, damnèd spot! Out, I say! One – two – why
then 'tis time to do't. Hell is murky. Fie, my lord, fie! a
soldier and afeard? What need we fear who knows it,
35 when none can call our pow'r to accompt? Yet who
would have thought the old man to have had so much
blood in him?

Doctor. Do you mark that?

Lady. The Thane of Fife had a wife. Where is she now?
40 What, will these hands ne'er be clean? No more o' that,
my lord, no more o' that! You mar all with this
starting.

Doctor. Go to, go to! You have known what you should
not.

45 *Gentlewoman.* She has spoke what she should not, I am sure
of that. Heaven knows what she has known.

Lady. Here's the smell of the blood still. All the perfumes
of Arabia will not sweeten this little hand. Oh, oh, oh!

Doctor. What a sigh is there! The heart is sorely charged.

50 *Gentlewoman.* I would not have such a heart in my bosom
for the dignity of the whole body.

Doctor. Well, well, well.

Gentlewoman. Pray God it be, sir.

Doctor. This disease is beyond my practice. Yet I have
55 known those which have walked in their sleep who have
died holily in their beds.

Lady. Wash your hands, put on your nightgown, look not
so pale! I tell you yet again, Banquo's buried. He cannot
come out on's grave.

60 *Doctor.* Even so?

Lady. To bed, to bed! There's knocking at the gate. Come,

---

35 *call our pow'r to accompt* call to account anyone so powerful as we
42 *starting* startled movements   49 *charged* laden   54 *practice* professional
competence

come, come, come, give me your hand! What's done
cannot be undone. To bed, to bed, to bed! *Exit.*

Doctor. Will she go now to bed?

Gentlewoman. Directly. 65

Doctor. Foul whisp'rings are abroad. Unnatural deeds
 Do breed unnatural troubles. Infected minds
 To their deaf pillows will discharge their secrets.
 More needs she the divine than the physician.
 God, God forgive us all! Look after her; 70
 Remove from her the means of all annoyance,
 And still keep eyes upon her. So good night.
 My mind she has mated, and amazed my sight.
 I think, but dare not speak.

Gentlewoman. Good night, good doctor.

Exeunt.

Drum and Colors. Enter Menteith, Caithness, Angus, **V, ii**
 Lennox, Soldiers.

Menteith. The English pow'r is near, led on by Malcolm,
 His uncle Siward, and the good Macduff.
 Revenges burn in them; for their dear causes
 Would to the bleeding and the grim alarm
 Excite the mortified man.

Angus. Near Birnam Wood 5
 Shall we well meet them; that way are they coming.

Caithness. Who knows if Donalbain be with his brother?

Lennox. For certain, sir, he is not. I have a file
 Of all the gentry. There is Siward's son

---

71 *annoyance* self-injury 73 *mated* bemused V, ii, 4 *bleeding* blood of
battle 5 *Excite* incite *mortified* dead 6 *well* surely 8 *file* list

10 And many unrough youths that even now
  Protest their first of manhood.

Menteith.   What does the tyrant?

Caithness. Great Dunsinane he strongly fortifies.
  Some say he's mad; others, that lesser hate him,
  Do call it valiant fury; but for certain
15 He cannot buckle his distempered cause
  Within the belt of rule.

Angus.   Now does he feel
  His secret murders sticking on his hands.
  Now minutely revolts upbraid his faith-breach.
  Those he commands move only in command,
20 Nothing in love. Now does he feel his title
  Hang loose about him, like a giant's robe
  Upon a dwarfish thief.

Menteith.   Who then shall blame
  His pestered senses to recoil and start,
  When all that is within him does condemn
  Itself for being there?

25 *Caithness.*   Well, march we on
  To give obedience where 'tis truly owed.
  Meet we the med'cine of the sickly weal;
  And with him pour we in our country's purge
  Each drop of us.

Lennox.   Or so much as it needs
30 To dew the sovereign flower and drown the weeds.
  Make we our march towards Birnam. *Exeunt, marching.*

10 *unrough* unbearded 11 *Protest* assert 15 *distempered* disease-swollen
16 *rule* reason 18 *minutely* every minute *revolts* rebellions 23 *pestered*
tormented 27 *med'cine* cure (i.e. Malcolm) *weal* commonwealth
30 *dew* water

Enter Macbeth, Doctor, and Attendants.

Macbeth. Bring me no more reports. Let them fly all!
  Till Birnam Wood remove to Dunsinane,
  I cannot taint with fear. What's the boy Malcolm?
  Was he not born of woman? The spirits that know
  All mortal consequences have pronounced me thus:
  'Fear not, Macbeth. No man that's born of woman
  Shall e'er have power upon thee.' Then fly, false thanes,
  And mingle with the English epicures.
  The mind I sway by and the heart I bear
  Shall never sag with doubt nor shake with fear.   10

Enter Servant.

  The devil damn thee black, thou cream-faced loon!
  Where got'st thou that goose look?
Servant. There is ten thousand —
Macbeth.   Geese, villain?
Servant.   Soldiers, sir.
Macbeth. Go prick thy face and over-red thy fear,
  Thou lily-livered boy. What soldiers, patch?   15
  Death of thy soul! those linen cheeks of thine
  Are counsellors to fear. What soldiers, whey-face?
Servant. The English force, so please you.
Macbeth. Take thy face hence.   *[Exit Servant.]*
                            Seyton! — I am sick at heart,
  When I behold — Seyton, I say! — This push   20
  Will cheer me ever, or disseat me now.
  I have lived long enough. My way of life
  Is fall'n into the sear, the yellow leaf,

V, iii, 3 *taint* become tainted   5 *consequences* sequence of events   8 *English epicures* (i.e. as compared with the austerely-living Scots)   9 *sway* direct myself   11 *loon* lout   14 *over-red thy fear* i.e. paint red over your fearful pallor   15 *patch* fool   20 *push* struggle   23 *sear* dry, withered

And that which should accompany old age,
25 As honor, love, obedience, troops of friends,
I must not look to have; but, in their stead,
Curses not loud but deep, mouth-honor, breath,
Which the poor heart would fain deny, and dare not.
Seyton!

Enter Seyton.

Seyton. What's your gracious pleasure?
30 *Macbeth.*   What news more?
Seyton. All is confirmed, my lord, which was reported.
Macbeth. I'll fight till from my bones my flesh be hacked.
Give me my armor.
Seyton.   'Tis not needed yet.
Macbeth. I'll put it on.
35 Send out moe horses, skirr the country round,
Hang those that talk of fear. Give me mine armor.
How does your patient, doctor?
Doctor.   Not so sick, my lord,
As she is troubled with thick-coming fancies
That keep her from her rest.
Macbeth.   Cure her of that!
40 Canst thou not minister to a mind diseased,
Pluck from the memory a rooted sorrow,
Raze out the written troubles of the brain,
And with some sweet oblivious antidote
Cleanse the stuffed bosom of that perilous stuff
Which weighs upon the heart?
45 *Doctor.*   Therein the patient
Must minister to himself.
Macbeth. Throw physic to the dogs, I'll none of it!

---

35 *moe* more *skirr* scour 42 *Raze* erase 43 *oblivious antidote* opiate,
medicine of forgetfulness 44 *stuffed* choked up 47 *physic* medicine

Come, put mine armor on. Give me my staff.
Seyton, send out. — Doctor, the thanes fly from me. —
Come, sir, dispatch. — If thou couldst, doctor, cast   50
The water of my land, find her disease,
And purge it to a sound and pristine health,
I would applaud thee to the very echo,
That should applaud again. — Pull't off, I say. —
What rhubarb, senna, or what purgative drug   55
Would scour these English hence? Hear'st thou of them?
Doctor. Ay, my good lord. Your royal preparation
Makes us hear something.
Macbeth.   Bring it after me!
I will not be afraid of death and bane
Till Birnam Forest come to Dunsinane.   60
                              Exeunt [all but the Doctor.]
Doctor. Were I from Dunsinane away and clear,
Profit again should hardly draw me here.   *[Exit.]*

Drum and Colors. Enter Malcolm, Siward, Macduff,   V, iv
    Siward's Son, Menteith, Caithness, Angus, [Lennox,
    Ross,] and Soldiers, marching.

Malcolm. Cousins, I hope the days are near at hand
    That chambers will be safe.
Menteith.   We doubt it nothing.
Siward. What wood is this before us?
Menteith.   The Wood of Birnam.
Malcolm. Let every soldier hew him down a bough

---

50 *dispatch* hasten   50–51 *cast . . . water* analyze the urine   58 *it* i.e. the remainder of the armor   59 *bane* destruction   V, iv, 2 *That chambers* when
sleeping-chambers   *nothing* not at all

5   And bear't before him. Thereby shall we shadow
     The numbers of our host and make discovery
     Err in report of us.
Soldiers.   It shall be done.
Siward. We learn no other but the confident tyrant
     Keeps still in Dunsinane and will endure
     Our setting down before't.
10 *Malcolm.*   'Tis his main hope,
     For where there is advantage to be given
     Both more and less have given him the revolt,
     And none serve with him but constrainèd things
     Whose hearts are absent too.
Macduff.   Let our just censures
15   Attend the true event, and put we on
     Industrious soldiership.
Siward.   The time approaches
     That will with due decision make us know
     What we shall say we have and what we owe.
     Thoughts speculative their unsure hopes relate,
20   But certain issue strokes must arbitrate —
     Towards which advance the war.   *Exeunt, marching.*

V, v   *Enter Macbeth, Seyton, and Soldiers, with Drum and
           Colors.*

     Macbeth. Hang out our banners on the outward walls.
          The cry is still, 'They come!' Our castle's strength
          Will laugh a siege to scorn. Here let them lie

6 *discovery* i.e. reports by scouts   11 *advantage* opportunity   12 *more and
less* high and low   14 *just censures* impartial judgment   15 *Attend* await
put we on let us put on   19 *relate* convey   20 *certain issue* the definite out-
come   *arbitrate* decide   21 *war* army   V, v, 2 *still* always

Till famine and the ague eat them up.
Were they not forced with those that should be ours,   5
We might have met them dareful, beard to beard,
And beat them backward home.   *A cry within of women.*
                              What is that noise?
Seyton. It is the cry of women, my good lord.   *[Exit.]*
Macbeth. I have almost forgot the taste of fears.
The time has been my senses would have cooled   10
To hear a night-shriek, and my fell of hair
Would at a dismal treatise rouse and stir
As life were in't. I have supped full with horrors.
Direness, familiar to my slaughterous thoughts,
Cannot once start me.

                    [Enter Seyton.]
                    Wherefore was that cry?   15
Seyton. The Queen, my lord, is dead.
Macbeth. She should have died hereafter:
There would have been a time for such a word.
To-morrow, and to-morrow, and to-morrow
Creeps in this petty pace from day to day   20
To the last syllable of recorded time,
And all our yesterdays have lighted fools
The way to dusty death. Out, out, brief candle!
Life's but a walking shadow, a poor player
That struts and frets his hour upon the stage   25
And then is heard no more. It is a tale
Told by an idiot, full of sound and fury,
Signifying nothing.

                    Enter a Messenger.

Thou com'st to use thy tongue: thy story quickly!

5 *forced* reinforced   11 *fell* pelt   12 *treatise* story   14 *Direness* horror
15 *start me* make me start

107

30 *Messenger.* Gracious my lord,
　　I should report that which I say I saw,
　　But know not how to do't.
　Macbeth.　　　　　　　　　Well, say, sir.
　Messenger. As I did stand my watch upon the hill,
　　I looked toward Birnam, and anon methought
　　The wood began to move.
35 *Macbeth.*　　　　　　　　Liar and slave!
　Messenger. Let me endure your wrath if't be not so.
　　Within this three mile may you see it coming.
　　I say, a moving grove.
　Macbeth.　　　　　　　If thou speak'st false,
　　Upon the next tree shalt thou hang alive
40　Till famine cling thee. If thy speech be sooth,
　　I care not if thou dost for me as much.
　　I pull in resolution, and begin
　　To doubt th' equivocation of the fiend,
　　That lies like truth. 'Fear not, till Birnam Wood
45　Do come to Dunsinane!' and now a wood
　　Comes toward Dunsinane. Arm, arm, and out!
　　If this which he avouches does appear,
　　There is nor flying hence nor tarrying here.
　　I 'gin to be aweary of the sun,
50　And wish th' estate o' th' world were now undone.
　　Ring the alarum bell! Blow wind, come wrack,
　　At least we'll die with harness on our back.　　*Exeunt.*

31 *say* i.e. affirm　　40 *cling* shrivel *sooth* truth　　42 *pull in* curb, check
43 *doubt* suspect *equivocation* double-talk　　47 *avouches* affirms　　52 *harness* armor

Drum and Colors. Enter Malcolm, Siward, Macduff, and   **V, vi**
   their Army, with boughs.

Malcolm. Now near enough. Your leavy screens throw
   down
   And show like those you are. You, worthy uncle,
   Shall with my cousin, your right noble son,
   Lead our first battle. Worthy Macduff and we
   Shall take upon's what else remains to do,   5
   According to our order.
Siward.   Fare you well.
   Do we but find the tyrant's power to-night,
   Let us be beaten if we cannot fight.
Macduff. Make all our trumpets speak, give them all breath,
   Those clamorous harbingers of blood and death.   10
                              Exeunt. Alarums continued.

Enter Macbeth.   **V, vii**

Macbeth. They have tied me to a stake. I cannot fly,
   But bear-like I must fight the course. What's he
   That was not born of woman? Such a one
   Am I to fear, or none.

Enter Young Siward.

Young Siward. What is thy name?
Macbeth.   Thou'lt be afraid to hear it.   5
Young Siward. No, though thou call'st thyself a hotter name
   Than any is in hell.

V, vi, 4 *battle* battalion   6 *order* battle-plan   7 *power* forces   V, vii, 2 *course*
attack (like a bear tied to a stake and baited by dogs or men)

Macbeth.   My name's Macbeth.

Young Siward. The devil himself could not pronounce a title
More hateful to mine ear.

Macbeth.   No, nor more fearful.

10 *Young Siward.* Thou liest, abhorrèd tyrant! With my sword
I'll prove the lie thou speak'st.

                        Fight, and Young Siward slain.

Macbeth.   Thou wast born of woman.
But swords I smile at, weapons laugh to scorn,
Brandished by man that's of a woman born.   *Exit.*

                Alarums. Enter Macduff.

Macduff. That way the noise is. Tyrant, show thy face!
15 If thou beest slain and with no stroke of mine,
My wife and children's ghosts will haunt me still.
I cannot strike at wretched kerns, whose arms
Are hired to bear their staves. Either thou, Macbeth,
Or else my sword with an unbattered edge
20 I sheathe again undeeded. There thou shouldst be:
By this great clatter one of greatest note
Seems bruited. Let me find him, Fortune,
And more I beg not!   *Exit. Alarums.*

                Enter Malcolm and Siward.

Siward. This way, my lord. The castle's gently rend'red:
25 The tyrant's people on both sides do fight,
The noble thanes do bravely in the war,
The day almost itself professes yours
And little is to do.

17 *kerns* soldiers of meanest rank   18 *staves* spears   20 *undeeded* not
glorified by deeds   22 *bruited* reported   24 *rend'red* surrendered   27 *itself professes* declares itself

Malcolm.   We have met with foes
  That strike beside us.
Siward.   Enter, sir, the castle. *Exeunt. Alarum.*

Enter Macbeth.   V, viii

Macbeth. Why should I play the Roman fool and die
  On mine own sword? Whiles I see lives, the gashes
  Do better upon them.

Enter Macduff.

Macduff.   Turn, hellhound, turn!
Macbeth. Of all men else I have avoided thee.
  But get thee back! My soul is too much charged   5
  With blood of thine already.
Macduff.   I have no words;
  My voice is in my sword, thou bloodier villain
  Than terms can give thee out!   *Fight. Alarum.*
Macbeth.   Thou losest labor.
  As easy mayst thou the intrenchant air
  With thy keen sword impress as make me bleed.   10
  Let fall thy blade on vulnerable crests.
  I bear a charmèd life, which must not yield
  To one of woman born.
Macduff.   Despair thy charm,
  And let the angel whom thou still hast served
  Tell thee, Macduff was from his mother's womb   15
  Untimely ripped.
Macbeth. Accursèd be that tongue that tells me so,
  For it hath cowed my better part of man!

29 *beside us* at our side (?) or, without trying to hit us (?)   V, viii, 2 *lives*
living bodies   5 *charged* burdened   9 *intrenchant* incapable of being
trenched (gashed)   10 *impress* leave a mark on   13 *Despair* despair of
14 *angel* i.e. of the host of Lucifer *still* always   18 *better part of man* most
manly side

And be these juggling fiends no more believed,
20   That palter with us in a double sense,
That keep the word of promise to our ear
And break it to our hope. I'll not fight with thee.
Macduff. Then yield thee, coward,
And live to be the show and gaze o' th' time.
25   We'll have thee, as our rarer monsters are,
Painted upon a pole, and underwrit
'Here may you see the tyrant.'
Macbeth.   I will not yield,
To kiss the ground before young Malcolm's feet
And to be baited with the rabble's curse.
30   Though Birnam Wood be come to Dunsinane,
And thou opposed, being of no woman born,
Yet I will try the last. Before my body
I throw my warlike shield. Lay on, Macduff,
And damned be him that first cries 'Hold, enough!'
                          Exeunt fighting. Alarums.
  [Re-]enter fighting, and Macbeth slain. [Exit Macduff.]

Retreat and flourish. Enter, with Drum and Colors, Mal-
   colm, Siward, Ross, Thanes, and Soldiers.

35 *Malcolm.* I would the friends we miss were safe arrived.
Siward. Some must go off; and yet, by these I see,
So great a day as this is cheaply bought.
Malcolm. Macduff is missing, and your noble son.
Ross. Your son, my lord, has paid a soldier's debt.

---

20 *palter* quibble   24 *gaze* sight   25 *monsters* freaks   26 *Painted upon a pole* pictured on a showman's banner   36 *go off* perish   *these* i.e. these here assembled

He only lived but till he was a man, 40
The which no sooner had his prowess confirmed
In the unshrinking station where he fought
But like a man he died.

Siward. Then he is dead?

Ross. Ay, and brought off the field. Your cause of sorrow
Must not be measured by his worth, for then 45
It hath no end.

Siward. Had he his hurts before?

Ross. Ay, on the front.

Siward. Why then, God's soldier be he.
Had I as many sons as I have hairs,
I would not wish them to a fairer death:
And so his knell is knolled.

Malcolm. He's worth more sorrow, 50
And that I'll spend for him.

Siward. He's worth no more.
They say he parted well and paid his score,
And so, God be with him. Here comes newer comfort.

Enter Macduff, with Macbeth's head.

Macduff. Hail, King, for so thou art. Behold where stands
Th' usurper's cursèd head. The time is free. 55
I see thee compassed with thy kingdom's pearl,
That speak my salutation in their minds,
Whose voices I desire aloud with mine –
Hail, King of Scotland!

All. Hail, King of Scotland! *Flourish.*

Malcolm. We shall not spend a large expense of time 60
Before we reckon with your several loves

---

42 *unshrinking station* place from which he did not retreat 52 *parted*
departed *score* reckoning 55 *free* released from tyranny 56 *compassed*
surrounded 61 *reckon* come to an accounting

And make us even with you. My Thanes and kinsmen,
Henceforth be Earls, the first that ever Scotland
In such an honor named. What's more to do
65   Which would be planted newly with the time –
As calling home our exiled friends abroad
That fled the snares of watchful tyranny,
Producing forth the cruel ministers
Of this dead butcher and his fiend-like queen,
70   Who (as 'tis thought) by self and violent hands
Took off her life – this, and what needful else
That calls upon us, by the grace of Grace
We will perform in measure, time, and place.
So thanks to all at once and to each one,
75   Whom we invite to see us crowned at Scone.

                              Flourish. Exeunt omnes.

62 *make us even with you* repay you   65 *would be planted newly with the
time* i.e. should be done at the outset of this new era   68 *ministers* agents
70 *self and violent* her own violent   73 *in measure* with decorum   *time,
and place* at the proper time and place

114

Appendix: List of Emendations

Except for extensive relineation, the following list of emendations indicates the only material departures from the Folio text. Most of the corrections first appeared in the later folios or in eighteenth-century editions.

I, i, 9–11 *2 Witch . . . air* (In the Folio these lines form a single speech attributed to "All.")

I, ii, 13 *gallowglasses* gallowgrosses   14 *quarrel* quarry   26 *thunders break* thunders   56 *point rebellious, arm* point, rebellious arm

I, iii, 32 *weird* weyward (also at I, v, 7; II, i, 20. "weyard" at III, i, 2; III, iv, 133; IV, i, 136.)   39 *Forres* Soris   98 *came* can   109 *borrowed* borrowèd

I, iv, 1 *Are* Or

I, vi, 4 *martlet* barlet   5 *loved* lovèd   9 *most* must

I, vii, 6 *shoal* school   47 *do* no   68 *lie* lies

II, i, 55 *strides* sides   56 *sure* sowre   57 *way they* they may

II, ii, 13 S.D. *Enter Macbeth* (appears after line 8 in Folio)

III, iv, 78 *time* times   135 *worst. For* worst, for   144 *in deed* indeed

III, v 124 *son* sons   38 *the* their

IV, i, 59 *germens* Germaine *all together* altogether   93 *Dunsinane* Dunsmane   98 *Birnam* Birnan (also at V, ii, 5, 31; V, iii, 2, 60; V, iv, 3; V, v, 34, 44; V, viii, 30)   111 S.D. *Kings and Banquo, last* Kings, and Banquo last   119 *eighth* eight

IV, ii, 22 *none* move   30 S.D. *Exit* Exit Ross   72 S.D. *Exit* Exit Messenger

IV, iii, 4 *downfall'n* downfall   15 *deserve* discerne   107 *accursed* accust   133 *thy here-approach* they here approach   235 *tune* time

V, i, 1 *two* too

V, iii, 55 *senna* cyme

V, v, 39 *shalt* shall

V, vii, 19 *unbattered* unbatterèd

*Details of the
Pelican Shakespeare and
other Penguin books
follow.*

THE PELICAN SHAKESPEARE

General Editor: Alfred Harbage

Tragedies

Edited by Maynard Mack	ANTONY AND CLEOPATRA
Harry Levin	CORIOLANUS
Willard Farnham	HAMLET
S. F. Johnson	JULIUS CAESAR
Alfred Harbage	KING LEAR
Alfred Harbage	MACBETH
Gerald E. Bentley	OTHELLO
John E. Hankins	ROMEO AND JULIET
Charlton Hinman	TIMON OF ATHENS
Gustav Cross	TITUS ANDRONICUS

Comedies

Jonas Barish	ALL'S WELL THAT ENDS WELL
Ralph Sargent	AS YOU LIKE IT
Paul A. Jorgensen	THE COMEDY OF ERRORS
Robert B. Heilman	CYMBELINE
Alfred Harbage	LOVE'S LABOR'S LOST
R. C. Bald	MEASURE FOR MEASURE
Brents Stirling	THE MERCHANT OF VENICE
Fredson T. Bowers	THE MERRY WIVES OF WINDSOR
Madeleine Doran	A MIDSUMMER NIGHT'S DREAM
Josephine Waters Bennett	MUCH ADO ABOUT NOTHING
James McManaway	PERICLES
Richard Hosley	THE TAMING OF THE SHREW
Northrop Frye	THE TEMPEST
Virgil Whitaker	TROILUS AND CRESSIDA
Charles Prouty	TWELFTH NIGHT
Berners Jackson	TWO GENTLEMEN OF VERONA
Baldwin Maxwell	THE WINTER'S TALE

Histories and Poems

M. A. Shaaber	HENRY IV, PART I
Allan Chester	HENRY IV, PART II
Alfred Harbage	HENRY V
David Bevington	HENRY VI, PART I
George Williams	HENRY VI, PART II
Robert K. Turner, Jr.	HENRY VI, PART III
F. D. Hoeniger	HENRY VIII
Irving Ribner	KING JOHN
Matthew Black	RICHARD II
G. Blakemore Evans	RICHARD III
Richard Wilbur	THE POEMS
Douglas Bush	THE SONNETS

PLAYS BY BERNARD SHAW

*The following plays are published
in Penguin editions. Each play has the
complete text and the
author's preface*

CHAUCER: THE CANTERBURY TALES

A Modern Version By
Nevill Coghill

This is the first English work to be included in the Penguin Classics series of modern translations. When it was published it was widely acclaimed as a means of bringing Chaucer to thousands of people who would never have read him otherwise. Reviewers were quick to realize that Mr Coghill, who is a fellow of Exeter College, Oxford, was the right person to have attempted the task.

Punch offered very high praise by saying ' . . . this translation will remain a beloved classic until the language changes again sufficiently to call for another renaissance'. *The Manchester Guardian* found that 'Mr Coghill has achieved his aim that his translation should be considered as a poem and not as a crib'. And the most enthusiastic welcome came from *The Times Educational Supplement* which said, 'Altogether Mr Coghill's achievement is remarkable. He has been almost consistently successful and his practice carries out his theory and intentions. The bland, humorous, observing, and courtly spirit that informs the original is somehow preserved in a different idiom'.

THE PELICAN HISTORY OF ENGLAND

While each volume is complete in itself, the whole series, edited by J. E. Morpurgo, has been planned to provide an intelligent and consecutive guide to the development of English society in all its aspects. The eight volumes are:

THE GREEK MYTHS

Robert Graves

Not for over a century, since Smith's *Dictionary of Classical Mythology* first appeared, has the attempt been made to provide for the English reader a complete 'mythology,' in the sense of a retelling in modern terms of the Greek tales of gods and heroes. In the two volumes of this book Robert Graves, whose combination of classical scholarship and anthropological competence has already been so brilliantly demonstrated in *The White Goddess* and *Hercules, My Shipmate*, and his other novels, supplies the need. In nearly two hundred sections, it covers the Creation myths, the legends of the birth and lives of the great Olympians, the Theseus, Oedipus, and Heracles cycles, the Argonaut voyage, the tale of Troy, and much else.

All the scattered elements of each myth have been assembled into a harmonious narrative, which notes also many variants which may help to determine its ritual or historical meaning. Full references to the classical sources, and copious indexes, make the book as valuable to the scholar as to the general reader; and a full commentary to each myth explains and interprets the classical version in the light of to-day's archaeological and anthropological knowledge.

42
44
55 ✓

59

62

74

81

8L. crowned

97